"An excellent text for clinicians, s
will expand one's clinical reperto
creative and mindful approaches. ᵀʰᵉ author's fusion of psychoanalytic
conceptualization with creative, brain-based interventions is fresh and
engaging. Clients needing to heal from complex trauma deserve our very
best work – using this text enlarges one's clinical ability to facilitate
healing and wholeness. These texts are valuable additions to the libraries
of clinicians, students, researchers, schools, and organizations involved in
any aspect of trauma work."
Stephannee Standefer, PhD, LCPC, *Associate Program Director,*
Counseling@Northwestern

"Costello provides a thoughtful and thorough look at addressing the
vastness of trauma and social justice inequalities with Creative Mindfulness Techniques (CMT) specific to clinical trauma. This text provides
incredibly meaningful and practical ways to prepare and support mental
health counselors and counselors-in-training to be aware and intentional
when considering CMT for all aspects of clinical trauma."
Tonya Davis, PhD, LCPC (IL), *(she, her, hers), Clinical Training*
Director/Core Faculty, The Family Institute at Northwestern University

"This text is a comprehensive resource for clinicians working to expand
their understanding and practice of creative mindfulness techniques,
including meditation, journaling, and art-making. *Creative Mindfulness*
Techniques for Clinical Trauma Work offers a multifaceted context to
these critical practices, providing extensive evidence to support their
inclusion in our work with clients. Dr. Costello has woven the theoretical
and practical information together to create a timely and necessary
handbook for the professional mental health clinician working today."
Amy J. Seitlin, *ATR-P, LCMHCA*

Creative Mindfulness Techniques for Clinical Trauma Work

Using evidence-based creative mindfulness techniques (CMT), this book acts as a useful guide for clinical mental health practitioners seeking to build resilience levels in clients recovering from trauma. It examines the effectiveness of the CMT approach, providing applicable art therapy techniques to enhance the therapist's toolbox for clinical effectiveness.

Combining a psychodynamic and neurobiological clinical lens, this book helps practitioners recognize and utilize creativity in dealing with trauma exposure, its cultural considerations, and its consequences on the individual, family, and the system. It also provides insights into the neurophysiological impact of mindfulness techniques on the brain. Chapters explore the clinician's role in the treatment of trauma, wellness, and the building of resiliency, creativity, and alternative approaches to changing neural pathways, positive psychology, and more. A collection of narrative case studies and guidance for specific activities to be used with diverse clients ensures easy practical usage of the theories explored.

Clinical mental health practitioners who work with clients suffering from PTSD, clinical trauma, stress, and anxiety will find this book essential.

Corinna M. Costello, Ph.D., LCMHCS, ATR-BC is the director of student support and a core faculty member of clinical mental health at The Family Institute of Northwestern University. Dr. Costello also practices art therapy. She contributed chapters for *The Neuroeducation Toolbox* and *Encyclopedia of Couple and Family Therapy*. She has also written and presented extensively on PTSD, anxiety, resiliency, mindfulness, and art therapy.

Creative Mindfulness Techniques for Clinical Trauma Work

Insights and Applications for
Mental Health Practitioners

Corinna M. Costello

Routledge
Taylor & Francis Group

NEW YORK AND LONDON

First published 2022
by Routledge
605 Third Avenue, New York, NY 10158

and by Routledge
2 Park Square, Milton Park, Abingdon, Oxon, OX14 4RN

Routledge is an imprint of the Taylor & Francis Group, an Informa business

© 2022 Taylor & Francis

Library of Congress Cataloging-in-Publication Data
A catalog record for this title has been requested

ISBN: 978-0-367-46593-3 (hbk)
ISBN: 978-0-367-46592-6 (pbk)
ISBN: 978-1-003-03059-1 (ebk)

DOI: 10.4324/9781003030591

Typeset in Times New Roman
by MPS Limited, Dehradun

Memorialize

This book honors the memories of Harriet Malinowski Gallas and Jolene Kelly

Contents

Preface: Important Considerations for Creative Mindfulness in the Clinical Setting

Professional Disclaimers

As we begin this discussion of Creative Mindfulness Techniques in the mental health setting, the reader will find the language and the author's interchange of words to describe the processes associated with the client. The language may include such terms as individual, participant, supervisee, and artist. The reader will also note the language and the author's interchange of words to describe the processes associated with the clinician. The language may include such terms as mental health professional, supervisor, and facilitator. As you review this work, be mindful and honor your own professional and ethical guidelines. These ethical obligations safeguard both you as a mental health professional and the individual that you will be providing mental health treatment. Full disclosure: You will note my ethical guidelines include the American Art Therapy Association Ethical Principles for Art Therapists (AATA, 2017), the American Counseling Association Code of Ethics (ACA, 2020), American Mental Health Counseling Association (AMHCA, 2020), and the Art Therapy Credentials Board Code of Ethics, Conduct, and Disciplinary Procedures (ATCB, 2019).

Facilitator as Guide

An important consideration in the Creative Mindfulness technique is the impact of the mental health clinician or facilitator as a guide to navigating experiences related to trauma. As any mental health professional will note, the importance of creating a safe, therapeutic space, without pushing the individual beyond where they are ready to go, is of utmost ethical and professional consideration. As a facilitator of the creative process, it is necessary to be respectful of the individual's experience and of their varying degrees of discomfort while engaging in the creative moment. This uneasiness or 'resistance' can be a natural part of the process and is based on the creative individuals' levels of exposure to this approach, the individual levels of confidence, and their risk-taking abilities (Malchiodi, 1998).

Scope of Practice

As with any professional mental health counseling intervention, the scope of practice is an integral aspect of treatment. This book and the companion workbook "Healing from Clinical Trauma Using Creative Mindfulness Techniques" (Costello & Short, anticipated 2021) provides clinical knowledge, mental health information, and important resources to support the professional mental health clinician with some basic tools for utilizing creative mindfulness techniques with clients dealing with trauma. All professional mental health clinicians require extensive training to receive the necessary and proper skills to engage in clinical work. Adding creative aspects to clinical work does not make one an art therapist but does provide the clinician with more extensive therapeutic tools for the clinical toolbox.

A major element of the creative process is inherently risky to the creator. It is perilous to explore powerful emotional experiences through this different and unique approach. To incorporate the creative process into clinical work with trauma requires patience, understanding, and a highly supportive stance of the individual's experience. Proper preparation is integral for the interventions provided and awareness and responsiveness to the experiences of the individual is necessary. Always consider if this is within your scope of practice AND if your client is ready for these interventions. That is our ethical obligation to our clients engaging in mental health treatment.

Exclusions

Some exclusions to these creative mindful techniques involve the type and severity of mental health concerns that the client is experiencing. As with any clinical work that mental health counselors engage in, we always consider the needs of the client, and the level of care required for the client must be considered. Important questions to answer before starting clinical work with CMT include: am I ready to support my client in this manner? Do I have appropriate supervision and training for my clients and where will I go for more training and resources? Where do I go for more information and support for these techniques and specifically for the clients I will be work with? How will I handle negative responses to these interventions? There are many more questions we will encounter in our clinical work, but our focus will be on our ethical obligation to our clients engaging in mental health treatment.

This book is written by a professional art therapist and licensed mental health counselor who has recognized that creativity is a viable method to incorporate into the mental health treatment approach. For it to be effective, however, mental health clinicians must have a level of competence and confidence in these approaches. The clinical world of the mental health clinician is fraught with client experiences of stress and conflictual moments of traumatic exposures. Mental health clinicians who work in the field of mental health must be cognizant of the stressors that await them. When we begin the creative moment in the mental health setting, the clinician may feel vulnerability and uncertainty about the necessary steps for creative engagement in trauma treatment. The goals of this manuscript are to empower, inform, and support your clinical efforts of treating the traumatized client with alternative and evidence-based interventions.

References

American Art Therapy Association (AATA). (2017). Ethics, American Art Therapy Association. [Online]. *American Art Therapy Association.* Available at: https://arttherapy.org/wp-content/uploads/2017/06/Ethical-Principles-for-Art Therapists.pdf [Accessed December 30, 2020].

American Counseling Association. (2020). *2020 ACA code of ethics.* Alexandria, VA: American Counseling Association.

American Mental Health Counselors Association (AMHCA). (2020). *Code of Ethics.*

Art Therapy Credentials Board (ATCB). (2019). *Code of ethics, conduct, and disciplinary procedures.* Available at https://www.atcb.org/Ethics/ATCBCode. [Accessed 30 December 2020].

Malchiodi, C. A. (1998). *The art therapy sourcebook.* McGraw-Hill/Contemporary Books.

Acknowledgments

Thank you to Mark Costello and my children Nicholas, Bailey, and Kelly Costello.

Thank you to my colleague and friend, Beth Ann Short.

I am so appreciative of the students, clients, and supervisees that assisted in this writing endeavor. I am very grateful for your openness to the creative process.

Introduction

The *Creative Mindfulness Techniques for Clinical Trauma Work* and the companion workbook *Healing from Clinical Trauma Using Creative Mindfulness Techniques* (Costello & Short, 2021) explores the interventions of incorporating creativity and mindfulness into clinical mental health work. By reviewing the evidence, the reader will learn how to consider the safe and effective use of creative and mindful approaches within the clinical setting and understand why these aspects are important to the process of emotional healing within the human species. The interventions presented to support the strengthening of resiliency and wellness considerations in the clinical experience of trauma work.

In reviewing the evidence presented throughout the book *Creative Mindfulness Techniques for Clinical Trauma Work*, the reader will consider why it is important to incorporate some creative and mindful steps into their clinical work. Used in conjunction with the companion workbook *Healing from Clinical Trauma Using Creative Mindfulness Techniques* (Costello & Short, 2021), the reader will be presented with practical techniques and pragmatic steps to incorporate these interventions safely and effectively in the clinical setting.

In the book *Creative Mindfulness Techniques for Clinical Trauma Work*, we will explore the evidence to support the innate act of the creative process, and the impact of the central nervous system on our human survival response system. Creative Mindfulness techniques will be defined, we will anthropologically explore the human experience of creativity and examine how the *Homo sapiens* species have utilized creativity for communication, expression, and protection. The neurobiological ramifications of trauma on the body and brain will be discussed and we will examine how humans respond and adapt to stress and its impact over long periods of time.

Approaches to finding balance or *allostasis* within the central nervous system will be explored and the brain alterations created from neuroplasticity, stress-response behaviors, breathwork, and mindfulness. Further evidence will examine the importance of mindful approaches and how other researchers have viewed these mindful activities throughout history. We will discuss how other authors have incorporated creativity and mindfulness

DOI: 10.4324/9781003030591-101

techniques into their clinical work. Next, the considerations for building resiliency and the impact of the resilient construct from a neurophysiological perspective may have on the individual dealing with trauma. Finally, the book will provide case examples to demonstrate the utilization of the Creative Mindfulness Techniques. These examples include Creative Mindfulness Techniques for supervision purposes, self-awareness and cultural considerations, the integration of mindfulness, the traumatized client experience, journaling and thoughtful reflective narratives for self-reflection, and poetry for the professional development of a counselor.

The companion workbook *Healing from Clinical Trauma Using Creative Mindfulness Techniques* (Costello & Short, 2021) will provide ethical, cultural, social constructivism considerations for creativity and mindful approaches in clinical trauma work and consider potentially comorbid issues relevant to trauma. This workbook will offer strength-based techniques and healing approaches while guiding the experience through creativity and mindfulness techniques. It will provide mental health clinicians opportunities to utilize various techniques, in conjunction with mental health treatment, or as a companion homework approach.

The workbook explores the incorporation of creativity and mindfulness techniques through a process-driven approach. Also examined, is the attachment style presented in psychodynamic theory and art therapy, as well as the transitional object consideration of clinical focus. Next, the book explores the utilization of the art directive and concern for the material or media choice within the clinical experience. The processing of the 'experience' of creative moments as well as the 'product' created from the session will be discussed.

Mindfulness and being in the moment are examined from an unconscious perspective and the eight dimensions of wellness, including breathwork, and neurofeedback. The workbook will outline and describe the *Creative Mindfulness Technique* and steps for effectiveness, as well as explore direct examples of guided imagery and directives. Also provided in this workbook are steps for assisting clients impacted with self-esteem issues and art directives that increase self-confidence goals. The workbook will further discover various pragmatic examples of clinical techniques for use with clients dealing with various other mental health concerns and diagnoses including anxiety, unipolar and bipolar disorder, post-traumatic stress disorder (PTSD), grief and loss, and addiction concerns.

Corinna M. Costello and Beth Ann Short

Reference

Costello, C., & Short, B. A. (2021). *Healing from clinical trauma using creative mindfulness techniques*. New York, NY: Routledge and Press.

Statement of Aims

The objective of this book is to provide a compelling manual on how to engage in creative and mindful techniques that mental health professionals can safely and effectively utilize. The intention is to explore effective approaches for clinical work with traumatized clients by exploring therapeutic goals and neurobiologically informed interventions. Considering material choice and artistic presentation, the intention is to discover effective approaches for your clinical work with your traumatized clients.

As a registered and board-certified art therapist and a psychodynamic psychotherapist, my creative approach and use of art therapy language is steeped in the traditions of the early life experience. The focus of the psychodynamic tradition relies on the individual's ability to gain self-awareness and understanding of their thoughts, feelings, and beliefs as well as their connections to early childhood experiences. The therapist skillfully guides the individual to the chronic conflicts from the past. The unresolved issue is firmly rooted in the individual's unconscious mind and must be brought out to conscious self-awareness for a corrective emotional experience and for new learning to occur.

The reader will note an affinity for person-centered counseling or client-centered counseling developed by Carl Rogers, which utilizes a non-authoritative approach to therapy and allows the individual to lead the process of discovery for their own solutions (Rogers, 1942; Rogers & Carmichael, 2014). The therapist acts as a facilitator or a guide to the therapeutic process and supports the individual in building self-confidence and identity. The approach teaches the individual to trust their own decision-making process and encourages healthy interpersonal relationships.

Also of note is the psychodynamic approach to the clinical experience. Psychodynamic psychotherapy focuses on the psychological roots of the emotional suffering of an individual. Through aspects related to self-reflection and self-examination, the relationship between client and therapist reveals the problematic concerns from attachment approaches established in earlier development. By examining the client's responses to the therapist in the 'here and now' relationship, the past attachment styles will be revealed,

DOI: 10.4324/9781003030591-102

and earlier traumas will be shared. The goal of psychodynamic psychotherapy is to help clients rework earlier experiences, create opportunities for corrective emotional experiences, and to assist in healthier approaches to interpersonal relationships.

Over the course of my clinical career, I have found the utilization of creativity and intentional mindfulness techniques highly effective in supporting a strength-based, self-reflective process. Creativity and mindfulness aid the individual in navigating aspects of risk, encouraging *flow* experiences, and supporting opportunities for corrective emotional experiences. The belief that the root cause of human behavior is buried deep within the unconscious mind and the emotional work of discovering and reworking the thought is central to the psychodynamic process. That process of exploration is encouraged and supported throughout the creative mindfulness technique.

References

Rogers, C. R. (1942). *Counseling and psychotherapy: Newer concepts in practice.* Houghton Mifflin.
Rogers, C. R., & Carmichael, L. (2014). *Counseling and psychotherapy: Newer concepts inpractice.* Riverside Press.

1 Introduction of the Creative Mindfulness Approach

I remember attending an art therapy conference several years ago. The speaker began presenting on the neuronal activity of the human brain. On the giant screen in the front, the audience saw large neuronal scans of a human brain. I remember the "aha" moment. It was my first time experiencing a large room of 300 people and hearing no discernable sound. At that moment, all I could hear was a large group of curious people simultaneously gasping for air in the same instant.

That moment stands out to me in my professional career in mental health counseling and art therapy. There was visual evidence or *proof* of what happens to the brain during intentional creative moments. On the large screen, I could see the neurons firing and wiring in action. There was a noticeable difference in the amount and the movement of the neurons and the neuronal pathways as the individual engaged in the creative activity. The treatment of making art and being creative was causing an alteration in the neurophysiology of the brain.

This moment in time was an affirmation of what art therapists and expressive arts therapists have known. The profession was waiting for science to catch up to our instincts to create. That is the moment when I knew others needed to be cognizant of the role of creativity; and the art process and techniques provided in mental health treatment. My professional quest has focused on continuing that *aha* moment for others to experience and understand. The processes involved in creative activity can serve to improve the human experience and the human condition.

Why Art and Creativity?

One thoughtful consideration in this evolving discussion is why does art and creativity matter? I think, now more than ever, our safety, our self-expression, our continued life responses to trauma matters. As counselors, parents, teachers, and as emotional beings, what we experience and how we navigate those experiences matter. We do not experience the world alone, and our innate connectedness to those around us, and our impact on them holds great importance. Art is a thoughtful extension of

DOI: 10.4324/9781003030591-1

the human experience, and the art we create through trauma healing serves as a long-lasting reminder that, through difficulty and triumph, we exist, and we can grow.

Art serves as nonverbal communication, a strong connection between the private worlds of the mind of the creator. Through art, we express, we heal, and we learn. So, when I am asked, "Why art?" I look to the paintings, the sculptures, back to the early cave drawings of humans who were around long before me and will remain long after I am gone, and I am reminded of the intense power these expressions hold; this communication approach driven by an innate need to share, remains part of the human experience.

Creativity largely impacts the outcome of art and our artistic expression. Creativity is the driving force of the shape art takes on. Inspiration may signal that initial spark, but creativity itself is what moves the artist's hands to make. In this book, we define creativity as the ability to make something meaningful and thought-provoking out of simple materials. In essence, to add to the artist's contemplative narrative.

Creative Mindfulness Approach

As we begin this exploration, consider what the mental health clinician might need for feelings of competence and confidence, in incorporating creativity into the clinical experience? Understand what traumatized individuals are seeking from treatment and what will be essential for clinical effectiveness? How will the reader engage in aspects of creative thinking that will support the individual in their creative process? We will begin our exploration of some basic concepts of humanity from a biological and neurophysiological process, and the impact of these concerns on the evolution of the human experience.

Traumatized Individual and Verbal Therapy

Let us begin this discussion with a moment that the mental health clinician may experience in their professional work. The traumatized individual enters the session and maintains a tearful and forlorn expression on her face. She immediately takes in a deep breath of oxygen. The silence of this moment is broken by the intake sound. Next, the clinician employs the counseling micro skill of silence, which is one of the basic foundational skills utilized in effective helping relationships. The silence at the moment allows the traumatized individual to "feel" those painful feelings that reside in the deeper regions of their brain's amygdala. Thus, triggering a mirror neuron response in the clinician. The clinician begins to "feel" the struggles within their own physical body and experiences physical tightness in the chest region, as well stress and tension in the shoulders. The clinician provides a verbal, self-disclosure statement about the mirror neurons that are being activated at the moment. This is the perspective of the mental health process of the verbal mental health clinician.

The next step in the clinical experience might be to focus on the disconnect from the feeling of *vulnerability* to experiencing *safety*. Confronting this discrepancy through immediacy and shifting the experience to a strength-based moment is important. Creating a corrective emotional experience for the individual rests in the process of feeling vulnerable and shifting to the feeling of 'safe' in this instant. The clinician must utilize effective, therapeutic, and evidenced-based clinical skills to engage the individual which allows them to alter the feeling of *scared* into the feeling of *empowerment*.

Mental health clinicians are constantly seeking to provide the most effective and evidence-based approaches for the treatment of the trauma experience. Verbal psychotherapy has served and will continue to aid the traumatized individual in these moments. However, this exploration will further examine alternative, evidence-based treatment approaches and explore the effectiveness of these approaches in assisting traumatized individuals.

Many mental health clinicians are seeking effective alternative approaches but struggle with the process of integration into the clinical experience. This discussion serves to provide evidence of support for these creative and mindful approaches; and the companion book, *Healing from Clinical Trauma Using Creative Mindfulness Techniques* (Costello & Short, anticipated 2021) provides pragmatic and direct usage for incorporation of these processes. Let us begin the conversation by defining the terminology for the Creative Mindfulness technique, any subsequent language involved, and the exploration into the self-reflective and self-actualizing process for healing.

The Creative Mindfulness technique is the act of paying attention to purpose, to an individual's present moment in time, and non-judgmentally letting creative experiences unfold. Through this mindful act, the creative experience of originality and meaning is determined by the creator (Costello, 2015). The goal of this interactive method is to increase psychological health and develop self-actualization skills for the traumatized individual. The use of intentional creative techniques in conjunction with mindfulness activity serves to mitigate the physiological responses of the body to trauma and rework the neurophysiological activity of the brain. This process of rewiring the neural pathways leads to adaptation and resiliency pattern identification. Strength-based or resilient approaches can support and enhance the neuronal alterations of the traumatized client's brain. Let us revisit the traumatized individual experience and incorporate techniques of Creative Mindfulness into the same clinical situation.

Traumatized Individual and Creative Mindfulness

The traumatized client maintains a tearful and forlorn expression on her face and immediately takes in a deep breath. The silence of this moment is broken by the client's subtle intake of oxygen. Next, the clinician employs the counseling micro skill of silence, which is one of the basic foundational skills utilized in effective helping relationships. The silence at the moment allows the client to *feel* those painful feelings that reside in the deeper regions of the brain's amygdala. The mental health clinician through support and without judgment offers the client paper and a pencil to write a poem about their current emotion. The mental health clinician acknowledges the mirror neuron response as they themselves begin to *feel* the struggles within their own body and experience physical tightness in the chest and stress and tension in the shoulders.

The client is encouraged to move her arms and her body to prepare for the physical nature of these feelings as well as the internalized feeling of the emotion. Within several thoughtful moments, the individual begins moving the pencil around on the paper. The ideas become *released* from the creator. The individual feels the physical motion of their body as their hands and arms move, their eyes transverse the page, the sound of material on paper penetrates the eardrum, and the experience of emotion is transformed into something different. The movement of the body and the mental response of taking the painful concepts and allowing them to be readjusted outside of the client's self.

And here, the process of sublimation begins. Sublimation is the psychodynamic defense mechanism that takes the unacceptable urges and alters the response to more socially appropriate utilization of the energy. At this moment, the client is altering their response and a new experience is starting to take shape. The client can verbalize the trauma memory or visually create the emotional expression of the physiological experience and subsequently rework the neuronal pathways within the brain. This process supports the neuroplasticity of the client's brain. Through the process of reworking the experience, new or alternative neuronal pathways are created.

The mental health clinician verbally provides a visual descriptive statement about what the client has just created. Perhaps they offer a reflection of a feeling statement about the emotion connected to the creation. Here the clinician may even offer a self-disclosure statement about what the clinician is feeling and experiencing as they are responding to the creative expression of the client. This is the perspective of the mental health process utilizing creative and mindful approaches to the mental health session.

The next step in the clinical experience might be to focus on the disconnect from the feeling of *vulnerability* to a different feeling of *safety* by confronting this discrepancy through immediacy and shifting the experience to a strength-based moment. Creating a corrective emotional experience for the client rests in the process of feeling vulnerable and *safe* in this moment. Or connecting the emotional content to the physical response of the client's body and empowering this moment in time. The clinician must utilize effective, therapeutic, and evidenced-based clinical skills to engage the client and allow them to transverse from feeling *scared* into feeling *empowered*. The creative mindful process activates multiple areas of the brain, and with mental health support, aids in reworking the neuronal pathways of the client's brain and emotional experience of the trauma content.

The Importance of the Human Experience through Anthropology

From a behavioral standpoint, the human species has survived and thrived because of our innate danger stress response system called *the central nervous system*. In this manuscript, we seek to better understand the human biological response of survival and appreciate those experiences that are revealed in our ancient art history. We shall review the processes involved in making art for expression, communication, or utility products created by craftsmen. Through understanding the qualities of the ancient and contemporary human experience, we will examine what it means to *be human* and the impact that *humanity* has on the individual, the system, and the community.

Prior to the advent of the written language, the utilization of materials for the creation of images was important in the recording of history. These pictorial images were called *cuneiform* which is Latin for 'cuneus', meaning 'wedge', and was begun around 3500 years BCE. This ancient writing system gradually became a complex system of characters that represented the dawn of the earliest written language.

History has demonstrated that art and symbolic expression have important societal aspects and represent a "basic human urge, a trait of our species as natural as language, sex, social interaction, and aggression" (Malchiodi 1998, p. 21). The creative process has an inherent healing power, whether from the method of making art or the product that is created from within the maker.

Prehistoric evidence about early humans is gathered through the excavation of archeological sites and studying their geographic locations throughout the world. By reviewing our ancient history as evidenced in the archeological remains, we can begin to understand our creative and expressive origins.

Through interdisciplinary use of technology, researchers can study the anatomy of fossils and bones and genetic data generated by radiocarbon dating and remote sensing information. Used in conjunction with human evolutionary studies, much supportive information is gathered through the implementation of virtual reality (VR) systems, photogrammetry, and LIDAR for "light detection and ranging" to create topography maps. Topography maps allow researchers to understand what landmass areas would have looked like in terms of vegetation, textures, and lighting, and

Figure 1.1 Stonehenge Prehistoric Monument 2,500 BCE Photo permission from
C. Costello (2020) Stonehenge is a prehistoric stone monument in
Wiltshire, England, 2500 BCE.

shadows and understand their ecological function by examining the artifact scatter. One of the most frequently investigated archeological locations includes Stonehenge and its connected sites (Figure 1.1).

The binomial nomenclature identification for the family *Hominidae* and the human species is called *Homo sapiensand was named by the father of modern biological classification, Carl Linnaeus* (Linnæus, 1758). We are identified as the bipedal primate species that use locomotion or movement with two feet, and the only member of the genus *Homo* not extinct. Anthropological researchers have identified that the upper Paleolithic population of humans existed from 40,000 to 10,000 years BCE (before the common era). The *Cro-Magnon man*, now referred to as the *anatomically modern human* (AMH) is regarded as the prototype of the modern *Homo sapiens* in Europe. The early modern human ranges in phenotypes and are anatomically consistent with contemporary humans. These upper Paleolithic Europeans also demonstrated similar cognition, symbolic activity, and human anatomy as more contemporary humans (Sherwood et al., 2008).

The *Homo Sapiens* species has achieved large evolutionary gains because of cognitive growth related to survival activities. By engaging in fundamental biological survival behaviors such as plant gathering and hunting food, the species has exponentially grown in population. Toolmaking and language shared a basis in the human ability for complex goal-directed manual activity. *Homo sapiens* originated as an agrarian civilization, cultivating the land for farming purposes and evolving physical characteristics and behavioral modifications that support human existence in various unstable environments. These behaviors included making specialized and refined tools for fishing, spearing, and sewing, as well as learning to control fire and living in shelters (Stout et al., 2008).

The evolution of brain architecture is the "ultimate expression of neuroplasticity" according to Anderson and Finlay (2014). Researchers have compared the sizes of bone structure and skull sizes and found significant alterations. The anatomically modern humans (AMH) large brain size indicates the amount of stored information, axonal connectivity availability, and the ability to access concepts and cognitively manipulate them in the cortical regions (Sherwood et al., 2008). For millions of years, all humans have had to find their own food sources for survival. In this beginning era, archaic humans had robust bone structure and a thick skull with a prominent supraorbital ridge (brow ridge), and an absence of a prominent chin. Over time, the prehistoric *homo sapiens* brain and skeleton altered in size because of the changes in the associated behaviors that were connected to the survival process. The increase in brain size is connected to the amount of information, the availability of neurons to access concepts, and the ability to manipulate these concepts in the sensory, motor, and associative cortical regions of the brain.

Within the last 12,000 years, the *Homo sapiens* species transitioned from gathering plants and hunting animals into producing food and changing the environment. Because of these adaptations to a communal approach of hunting and gathering, the human skeleton continued to decrease in size (Morriss-Kay, 2010). From hunting and gathering of plants, the change occurred to a sedentary approach to food production. Farming and herding animals led to humans settling down in locations such as villages. These villages became towns and towns grew to become cities. This provided more food availability and a dramatic increase in the human population on Earth.

The earliest known creative behaviors were of decorating the human body with human body coloring with ochre, and the use and beads (Layton, 1991). The complexity of the human brain of anatomically modern humans (AMH) allowed the human species to interact with each other and with the environment in new and different ways. As these interactions occurred, it altered human brain development and strengthened different and alternative neuronal pathways (Sherwood et al., 2008).

Evolution and Brain Development

As the AMH continued to engage in problem-solving behaviors, new neural pathways and connections increased the complexity of the human

Figure 1.2 Ancient Egyptian Mummy 2600 BCE, Photo permission by C. Costello (2020) Displayed in Rijksmuseum van Oudheden, Amsterdam.

brain. With these behaviors, modern humans built social networks, sometimes including humans they have never even met before or exchanging resources and ideas over wide areas of the region. Through these connections, modern humans found ways to create art for symbolic reasons: to mark territory or tribe, for ritualized activities, as personal adornment, or for religious ideologies (Morriss-Kay, 2010). This communication of language and art supported the survival and cohesion of the early human social groups. The Ancient Egyptians practiced ritualized behaviors about death and the afterlife as evidenced by their mummification processes of their deceased (Figure 1.2).

Creative Expressions and Socialization

As the creative expressions are examined, consider the concept provided by Morriss-Kay that art requires a "social context" to have meaning (Morriss-Kay 2010, p. 173). The human experience created within art is a symbolically communicative system that is adaptive to individuals in the group and society. At this time, the artwork created utilized metaphors and images to communicate various ideas, but images shifted to words, language, and literacy; this altered the left hemispheric modes of thought and subsequently, the brain's neural organization (Shlain, 2005). The positive social aspects of creativity are thought to have shaped the evolutionary changing human brain including size, anatomy, and functional abilities (Dunbar and Shultz, 2007).

Anatomically modern humans were emigrating to every continent and vastly expanding their populations. As they migrated from Africa, regional styles altered based on environmental factors, different available materials, technical skills, and changes in climates (Morriss-Kay, 2010). The thematic content of the artwork created demonstrates two human drives that include the preservation of the individual as represented in hunting, animals, and food sources. The second theme involved images that preserved the species and included sex and fertility (Morriss-Kay, 2010). The creation of symbolic art that characterizes the beliefs of its creators is prevalent throughout the history of humans. According to Zaidel (2014), art serves the human experience through a "cohesive symbolic communicative system conveying cultural norms, history, ideas, and emotions" (p. 2). The painted triptych called the *Dombild Altarpiece* (Kolner Dombild) representing the late International Gothic period. The paneled work represents three realistic images of religious beliefs with brilliant colors and surface textures of illuminated manuscript quality (Figure 1.3).

Whether exploring the spiritual world or the real world of the human experience, creative expression has served to benefit the human experience through knowledge and understanding. The artwork and self-expression include the visual, tactile, and kinetic experiences and represent the personal language of the creator. Van Manen (1990) discussed how artists are involved in "giving shape to their lived experience, the products of art are, in a sense, lived experiences transformed into transcended configurations" (p. 74). Knowledge of our history allows for

Figure 1.3 Triptych Painting by Stefan Lochner of Mother Mary and the Baby Jesus, Cologne Cathedral, Germany 1400 CE, Photo permission C. Costello 2017, Photo of Triptych inside the Cologne Cathedral, Germany, 1440 CE.

Figure 1.4 Stained Glass from Cologne Cathedral, Germany, 1249 CE, Permission for a photograph from C. Costello (2015), One section of glass from the interior of the cathedral in Cologne, Germany.

an increased appreciation of the behavioral actions and responses of the human species when in an activated state of being. Figure 1.4 represents the spoils of war and the powerful patrons that support the local Christian church in Germany. Figure 1.5

Figure 1.5 Buddhist Image Art Institute of Chicago, Photo permission by C.
Costello, Art Institute of Chicago Museum, Buddha Shakyamuni Seated
in Meditation (Dhyanamudra), Chola period, about 12th century.

The large seated stone Buddhist sculpture represents the Buddha
Shakyamuni seated in meditation (Dyanamudra) approach to meditation
and deep enlightenment (Figure 1.5). The Buddha is one who has attained
Bodhi or wisdom which is the ideal state of intellectual and ethical per-
fection. As we focus on understanding the innate human response of art
and creativity as a thoughtful and historic extension of the human experience, let's connect this back to the important work of the mental
health clinician. The goal of the mental health clinician supporting
stressed or traumatized individuals is to provide the most effective and
evidence-based treatment approach and, to respond to clients where they
are at in the treatment process.

The Mental Health Clinician

Clinical mental health treatment traditionally utilizes verbal psychotherapy in this trauma process. These approaches focus on verbal or talk therapy as a response to a wide range of mental health concerns. The evidence supports this verbal psychodynamic psychotherapy treatment approach and is rooted in the revelation of the unconscious content of the client's psyche to reduce or alleviate the psychic tension (Shedler, 2012). When individuals become aware of these unresolved conflicts, they can consciously choose alternative options. This represents one of the main tenants in mental health; to empower individuals in making healthier choices and living life more effectively.

From a neuro-physiologically informed approach, are we missing the mark? What if there is an alternative, evidence-based treatment that aids in this deeply rooted approach that is effective in altering the trauma brain? Through supportive and empowerment treatment techniques, what if we can help reduce the neurophysiological symptomology and increase moments of self-care, wellness, and resiliency. By the incorporation of creativity and art, we can support trauma healing and growth opportunities in the traumatized client and as our history informs us, it is an innate behavior that is readily available to the human species.

References

Anderson, M. L., & Finlay, B. L. (2014). Allocating structure to function: The strong links between neuroplasticity and natural selection. *Frontiers in Human Neuroscience, 7*(918), 1–16.

Costello, C. (2015). *Developing resiliency practices in master's level counseling students through creative mindfulness training: An exploratory study.* ProQuest Dissertations Publishing.

Costello, C. M., & Short, B. A. (2021). *Healing from clinical trauma using creative mindfulness techniques.* New York, NY: Routledge and Press.

Dunbar, R., & Shultz, S. (2007). Evolution in the social brain. *Science, 317,* 1344–1347. DOI: 10.1126/science.1145463

Layton R. (1991). *The anthropology of art.* Cambridge: Cambridge University Press.

Linnæus, C. (1758). *Systema naturæ,* (vol. 1, No. part 1, p. 532). Stockholm: Laurentii Salvii.

Malchiodi, C. A. (1998). *The art therapy sourcebook.* McGraw-Hill/Contemporary Books.

Morriss-Kay, G. M. (2010). The evolution of human artistic creativity. *Journal of Anatomy, 216,* 158–176.

Shedler, J. (2012). The efficacy of psychodynamic psychotherapy. In R. A. Levy, J. S. Ablon & H. Kächele (Eds.), *Psychodynamic psychotherapy research: Evidence-based practice and practice-based evidence* (pp. 9–25). Humana Press - Springer. https://doi.org/10.1007/978-1-60761-792-1_2

Sherwood, C. C., Subiaul, F., & Zawidzki, T. W. (2008). A natural history of the human mind: Tracing evolutionary changes in brain and cognition. *Journal of Anatomy*, *212*(4), 426–454. https://doi.org/10.1111/j.1469-7580.2008.00868.x

Shlain, L. (2005). The alphabet versus the goddess: The conflict between word and image. *Journal of the American College of Surgeons*, *200*, 157–159. 10.1016/j.jamcollsurg.2004.10.016

Stout, D., Toth, N., Schick, K., & Chaminade, T. (2008). Neural correlates of early stone age toolmaking: Technology, language and cognition in human evolution. *Philosophical Transactions of the Royal Society B: Biological Sciences*, *363*, 1939–1949. DOI: 10.1098/rstb.2008.0001. PMID: 18292067; PMCID: PMC2606694.

Van Manen, M. (1990). *Researching lived experience: Human science for an action sensitive pedagogy*. Ontario State University of New York Press.

Zaidel, D. W. (2014). Creativity, brain, and art: Biological and neurological considerations. *Frontiers in Human Neuroscience*, *8*, 389. DOI: 10.3389/fnhum.2014.00389

2 Trauma Exposure

Introduction to the World of Trauma

The impact of trauma on the neurophysiology of the human body and brain is deleterious to the individual and the community. Trauma events may include accidents, physical conditions, and violence and are the direct result of the physical nature of the biological experience of living life. Traumatic events may occur from a single catastrophic event such as a medical intervention, a car accident, or witnessing a sudden traumatic death. Trauma exposure becomes complicated when it involves repeated traumatic experiences of domestic violence, child abuse, or military service. Also included in the scope of trauma are social justice inequalities and considerations that impact individuals based on their race, religion, sexual orientation, gender, socioeconomic status, and culture. Mental health treatment goals for traumatized clients include finding mental health professionals to support coping strategies and to regain levels of functioning lost during traumatic exposure or subsequent stressful events.

We will begin by examining the impact and the prevalence of trauma on the world and consider its effect on the human condition. Exposure to adverse experiences or traumatic events can be emotionally devastating, to the traumatized individual, the families, and the communities impacted by the traumatic situation. Millions of people around the world encounter mental health problems such as post-traumatic stress reactions, substance abuse, anxiety, and depression that are caused or worsened by other traumatic events and inequalities present around the world.

Global Impact of Trauma

There are several global events that are having a major negative impact around the world and leading to increased experiences of trauma. These events are impacting both the collective world as well as the safety and well-being of the individual. Research indicates the negative impact of mental health problems in low- and middle-income countries according to the World Health Organization (2009). We shall discuss these top events

DOI: 10.4324/9781003030591-2

because they create an increase in security concerns around the world that impact the well-being of its citizens, and cause a rise in cultural inequalities, liberties and freedoms injustices, social and systemic violence, and death.

A major issue that is having a huge impact across the globe is that atmospheric temperatures are rising and impacting climate change and causing more severe and dangerous weather. The impact of climate change is altering housing considerations and causing people to migrate to other regions of the world in search of alternative living situations. Along with issues of corruption of local and state governments in various parts of the world; exploitative practices are severely impacting the safety of its residents and their accessibility to resources.

Pollution is also impacting the oceans with litter and increasing the spread of disease, thus reducing access to clean water, and impacting resource acquisition. The limited availability of food and proper nutrition is causing food deserts and a food crisis, malnutrition, and hunger rates in various parts of the world. With the rising estimated global population, there will be a huge strain on current food production systems and with decreasing availability of agricultural land, this will directly impact the low and middle incomes countries the most.

More than 72 million school-age children throughout the world are not enrolled in primary education school. This fact can be attributed to inequality and marginalization as well as poverty. A lack of resources related to technology is impacting these children, and without necessary education and training, many individuals will struggle to find employment. Without employment opportunities, individuals and communities will experience a lack of necessary resources including food, clothing, transportation, and living conditions, and ultimately poverty.

In a 2010 World Health Organization (WHO, 2010) trauma study conducted in 21 countries, over 10% of respondents reported witnessing some form of violence (21.8%) or experiencing interpersonal violence (18.8%), accidents (17.7%), exposure to war (16.2%), or traumatic violence to a loved one (12.5%) (Stein et al., 2010). These various individual events are collectively affecting economic aspects around the world.

US Trauma Statistics

The trauma experience is impactful to the individuals, the families, the communities, and the countries that are exposed. More specifically to the United States, the National Institute for Mental Health statistics for the trauma response, or Post-Traumatic Stress Disorder (PTSD) indicates that 7%-8% percent of the United States population will have PTSD at some point in their lives and 5.2 million adults will be impacted by trauma (National Institute of Mental Health, 2013).

In fact, the leading cause of death for Americans between the ages of 1 through 44 years old are injuries and violence such as motor vehicle crashes, suicide, or homicides according to the Centers for Disease Control and Prevention [CDC] 2001-2018 National Center for Injury Prevention and Control. The trauma experience is widespread and mental health clinicians will be exposed, either through clients of trauma or from their own personal life situations.

COVID-19

At the time of this writing, the world is experiencing a worldwide pandemic of an infectious disease called coronavirus disease 2019, or COVID-19. SARS-CoV-2 is a severe acute respiratory syndrome and part of the coronavirus family (CoV). This strain of coronavirus is thought to have originated out of China in late December 2019 (CDC, 2020). Individuals infected have experienced symptoms of fever, coughing, and shortness of breath leading to more severe issues of pneumonia, multi-organ failure, severe acute respiratory syndrome, and even death, in more severe cases.

Many of the deaths from COVID-19 have severely impacted the elderly (aged 65 and over), those with pre-existing chronic health conditions, homeless individuals, and individuals living in care facilities. Individuals with chronic health conditions such as asthma, hypertension, diabetes, and chronic obstructive pulmonary disease are more susceptible to coronavirus infections (Ejaz et al., 2020), and individuals with comorbidity concerns have a higher chance of getting infected than the general population (Guan et al., 2020).

Globally, as of June 19, 2021, there have been 177,108,695 confirmed cases of COVID-19, including 3,840,223 deaths, reported on the World Health Organization Dashboard (CDC, 2020). These staggering numbers will continue to surge until our human behaviors for survival alter to include mask-wearing and social distancing during the pandemic, or until the scientists can determine a safe, effective vaccine and wage a massive vaccination effort. As of this writing, over 2 million Covid 19 vaccines have been administered worldwide.

Because of the novel coronavirus 2019 (COVID-19) pandemic, mental health and emotional issues are now among the foremost public health concerns throughout the world. Concern over the fear of infection or fear of death will have long-term ramifications on our communities, our culture, and our clients and will be a leading cause of mental health concerns for years to come. Consequently, many individuals are experiencing anxiety, anger, confusion, and posttraumatic symptoms at elevated levels (Mukhtar, 2020; Pakpour & Griffiths, 2020).

Neurobiological Experience

The impact of any perceived trauma exposure may alter the homeostasis of both brain neurochemistry and the individual's nervous system activation.

Maintaining a neurobiologically-informed understanding of the trauma response experienced by trauma clients is integral to providing ethical treatment approaches. The necessity of understanding the neurobiological experience has been identified by the American Mental Health Counselors Association (AMHCA, 2020; Council for Accreditation of Counseling and Related Educational Programs, 2009; Insel et al., 2010).

Informed trauma work involves knowing the emotional and behavioral manifestations as well as the physical impact within the body (Bicknell-Hentges & Lynch, 2009). With this knowledge, mental health professionals can modify their clinical mental health counseling techniques to effectively target specific treatment goals while integrating the neurosciences (Luke et al., 2019). Beeson and Field's (2017) identify neurocounseling as:

> A specialty within the counseling field, defined as the art and science of integrating neuroscience principles related to the nervous system and physiological processes underlying all human functioning into the practice of counseling for the purpose of enhancing clinical effectiveness in the screening and diagnosis of physiological functioning and mental disorders, treatment planning and delivery, evaluation of outcomes, and wellness promotion. (p. 74)

Comorbidity

There are inherent challenges to identifying the proper diagnostic criteria of PTSD since comorbidity is so high within the victimized PTSD population. Briere and Scott (2006) discussed the complexity of the traumatic and physical symptoms in the trauma experience, leading to a PTSD diagnosis may include violent personal assaults, accidents, natural or human-caused disasters, or military combat (American Psychiatric Association, 2013).

Post-Traumatic Stress Disorder

The official recognition of the term post-traumatic stress disorder (PTSD) as a diagnostic syndrome occurred in the publication of the Diagnostic and Statistical Manual of Mental Disorders (DSM-III; American Psychiatric Association, 1980). The study of trauma has increased and evolved since then and the most recent classification of traumatic exposure or Post-Traumatic Stress Disorder (PTSD) is defined by the American Psychiatric Association (APA, 2000) as:

> the direct personal experience of an event that involves actual or threatened death or serious injury, or other threat to one's physical

integrity; or witnessing an event that involves death, injury, or a threat to the physical integrity of another person; or learning about unexpected or violent death, serious harm, or threat of death or injury experienced by a family member or other close associate. (p. 463)

In 2013, the Diagnostic and Statistical Manual of Mental Disorders (5th ed.; DSM–5; American Psychiatric Association 2013) definition was updated with enhancements of post-traumatic stress disorder (PTSD) and the concepts related to trauma. The four symptoms of exposure to trauma and PTSD were identified as re-experiencing the events as a recurrent dream or flashback and heightened arousal impacting sleep and increasing a hyper-vigilance state. Another symptom may include negative thoughts, moods, or feelings which include a sense of blame for self or others. The final symptom is estrangement from others and a decreased interest in activities as well as an inability to remember key aspects of the event (APA, 2013).

Trauma Response

The individual response to trauma is unique to the individual's experience of the trauma, and the subsequent, responsiveness of others around the individual after the experience. As a result, some trauma clients may find positive meanings out of the trauma situation which leads to the strength-based acquisition of resilience and flexibility. Other traumatized individuals experience negativity and emotional pain that becomes a central defining moment for the individual. This severe emotional distress may lead to more maladaptive behaviors and dysfunctional emotional outcomes. However, there are many variables that impact the responsiveness of the individual to the trauma experience. These variables include the duration of the trauma experienced, the developmental age of the individual, any previous history of trauma exposures, social support, and culture surrounding the individual, any family history of psychiatric issues, and the level of emotional functioning prior to the experience of the trauma (Yehuda & McFarlane, 1996).

The traumatized individual's responsiveness may also be impacted by the emotional and physical proximity to the actual danger or the degree of perceived personal control of the event. Trauma events and experiences are viewed from two broad categories of "Acts of God" which involves natural disasters, accidents, and illness and where no one is responsible. The other category includes acts of humans that identify responsibility and involves premeditation, planning, and some amount of deliberateness. This may include genocide, combat, torture, and sexual and physical assault and is perpetrated by other individuals (Courtois & Gold, 2009). Both types of trauma will be impactful to the traumatized individual, but there may be variance in the level and severity of the emotional response.

The timing of the trauma exposure may affect the trauma response for some clients. The trauma or stress response may occur at the onset of the traumatic experience and in other cases, there may be after a delayed activation of PTSD symptoms. The "reactivation or exacerbation of post-traumatic symptoms may be triggered by anniversaries of the traumatic events" (Kluft et al., 2000, p. 4). Also, the timing of the treatment may occur directly after the event happens or it may begin many years after the trauma event. This will be a consideration in the process of the trauma treatment and the stress response.

Trauma Treatment

Through supportive and empowering approaches to healing, the treatment seeks to reduce the neurophysiological symptomology and increase self-care strategies, wellness approaches, and resiliency levels. However, as we have noted, trauma responses may vary, thus making trauma treatment challenging. With such variability, trauma treatment may be difficult; as the trauma experienced may be cumulative to the individual and convolute the clinical picture of the client being presented to the clinician (Kessler et al., 2005).

In some cases, the traumatized individual may repetitiously replay painful memories and modify the emotional response resulting in a gradual increase in tolerance. This may lead to healing through integration and acceptance of the experience. Others may use avoidance approaches that lead to dissociation which can serve the traumatized individual by aiding in organizing information or the compartmentalization of experiences. This will allow for an increase in the reduction of physiological responses of the body and brain. While other traumatized individuals may develop avoidance approaches with more persistent patterns of hyperarousal leading to a stress response. Over time, a Post-Traumatic Stress Disorder (PTSD) may develop (Horowitz, 1978) leading to more complexity in the treatment of trauma.

As we consider alternative treatment approaches, we shall remain vigilant about increasing positive responses and reducing the negative symptoms of trauma exposure. Creativity may be effective in stimulating the proactive approaches to healing by reducing the physiological responses, increasing the body's natural neurochemical expression, and altering the brain's neuronal firing. Creativity helps by altering an individual's way of thinking and feeling about a situation. These alternative methods of thought allow for the creation of new or different neuronal pathways, reduces the body's stress response system, provides separation and physical distance from the emotional content, and offer new insight and learning. In traditional talk therapy, the narrator "tells their story" with edits and versions of information, based on what the individual wants to share. The neurons fire and wire together based on a familiar pattern of communication. With creativity and mindfulness added to the process, new neuronal pathways are activated and may prevent the individual from consciously filtering or editing their reaction. As we are looking to enhance the natural aspects of this process of healing, let us explore the use of narration in the trauma individuals telling and retelling of their stories.

Cultural Considerations and Trauma

As we understand the experiences of trauma, we shall now examine how culture may impact the prevalence, the treatment, and the support system surrounding the traumatized individual. Culture influences the identification of the necessity for mental health treatment and the methods in which one seeks emotional support. The Office of Surgeon General (2001) identified the culture's impact on health, wellness, and illness as:

> whether people are motivated to seek treatment, how they cope with their symptoms, how supportive their families and communities are, where they seek help (mental health specialist, primary care provider, clergy, and/or traditional healer), the pathways they take to get services, and how well they fare in treatment. (p. 26)

Hechanova and Waelde (2017) examined cultural diversity and mental health and determined various areas for consideration. They found that *emotional expression* was a concern in that some cultures may identify a lack of balance in expression that may lead to disease. Further, there was a belief that talking about emotional issues may cause more painful feelings. *Shame* and *power* also played a significant role in the family unit and mental health. Another area involved the nature of *collectivism* and its impact as a supportive factor to resilience and coping. Finally, *spirituality and religion* are significant approaches to dealing with the disease.

Western Trauma Treatment Approaches

The Western philosophical treatment approach for trauma exposure was provided through the act of discussing the trauma for retrieval and review, and then reprocessing the emotions during the counseling session. However, some patients may respond with an exacerbation of symptoms (Van der Kolk et al., 1996). Trauma researchers understand how the retelling of the trauma experience for treatment purposes, when offered before the client is ready, may retraumatize the individual who is seeking help for their trauma.

Previous treatment approaches towards trauma have been geared towards a mono-culturally ethnocentric client and maintained little concern for issues related to diversity. "Since Freud developed the talking cure, psychotherapy has meant that clients must be able to verbalize their thoughts and feelings to a practitioner in order to receive the necessary help" (Sue & Sue, 2013, p. 180). Bicknell-Hentges & Lynch (2009) discussed how treating trauma was about the retelling of the trauma story which was "curative and necessary" in the treatment of the trauma. Consider how this treatment approach might impact a culture of people that have experienced generations of historical trauma by the European colonizers? This is the case with the Indigenous *First Nations* communities, and their personal experiences of a traumatic nature indicate the "complex, collective, cumulative, and intergenerational" psychosocial impacts on the culture (Gone, 2013).

Trauma may be experienced by the multicultural client who comes to the United States to escape political, socioeconomic, or religious persecution. The multicultural client may become a refugee or take on an immigrant status from their home country, thus leaving one traumatic experience for another. Mental health clinicians should be cognizant of the possibility of a client leaving an oppressive country or coming into a structural system of gender or cultural bias. Communication issues, reading social cues, and self-expression may be another concern that complicates and convolutes the treatment approach.

The individualized experience of treatment may need to focus on considerations of the morality of the traumatic experience, the response by the culture, and any pending legal action. Once the multicultural individual migrates out of their country and arrives in the new location, what experiences will they have? Any victimization of race, culture, or gender upon arriving in the new country, whether from acculturation or migration, may have an extended traumatic response. As a result, the mental health clinician may see various behavioral responses that include internalization and withdrawal from one culture or acting out with disregard towards another culture.

Cultural Considerations for Trauma Treatment

It is necessary that "cultural differences be appreciated and understood to arrive at a correct diagnostic impression and treatment plan" (Bhugra & Becker, 2005). Culture and cultural considerations are essential elements to an individual's narrative story. Valentine et al. (2009) discussed the complexity of the traumatic and physical symptoms in the traumatized client's life and its intersectionality with ethnicity. Smith (2004) defines culture and ethnicity as a group of people with a distinct socio-cultural experience that includes characteristic values, behaviors, and worldviews. Sociocultural experiences may be demonstrated through clothing, foods, customs, (beliefs) or traditions, languages, parenting beliefs, family structure, social hierarchy, gender-role expectations, and communication style (Capuzzi & Stauffer, 2016)

For treatment of trauma, Dan Siegel (2013) discussed how the "un-resolved trauma or loss can be resolved through integrating the processes of memory and narrative" (P. 176). All individuals have ethnicity or cultural background which is a part of their human experience. The utilization of sociocultural narratives may be an effective approach towards emotional healing from trauma. However, this does not have to be incorporated strictly within a verbal capacity. For example, in a study of the *Aboriginal healing projects* operating across Canada, the First Nation, Inuit, and Metis organizations and communities found that for those who have been disconnected from their culture, learning a traditional craft or how drumming was important for "re-connecting with their Aboriginal identity and, thus, toward healing" (Archibald & Dewar, 2010, p. 6).

Cultural Examples of Healing

Cultures have maintained their own traditions of treatment and should be considered within effective trauma treatment approaches (Adekson, 2017). For example, "many different cultures have healing traditions that activate and utilize physical movement and breath" (Ogden et al., 2006, xxiii). The role of activity and family or community relationships can be effective in communal acts of returning to the land such as hunting (Kirmayer et al., 2003). Other examples of movement and breathing include the Asian and African approaches of meditation, yoga, chi gong, and Tai Chi. In some cultures, art is incorporated into the daily experiences of life. Cameron (2010) found that indigenous Australians consider art as a daily practice of making meaning, rather than just an artistic "ideal." Other examples include Huss and Cwikel (2005) who examined the role of art therapy and arts-based research when working with the Bedouin women living in Israel who utilized the role of art therapy and arts-based research.

Cameron 2010Huss 2005Recognizing the importance of culture may allow for other effective treatment approaches to be incorporated. Healing practices and systems can be integrated into the provision of mental health services through community-based health systems and collaborative partnerships. In collectivist cultures, healing is inter-dependent on the health of every individual member in the group (Hechanova & Waelde, 2017). For example, the communal perspectives may include prayer, the interpretation of dreams, folklore, and burning sacred plants, using eagle feathers, herbal therapy, and ancestors' prayers, and are practiced by the Yoruba and Native Americans and First Nation Canadians (Adekson, 2017). This renewed focus on participation in traditional cultural practices may help to strengthen the collective identity and meaning-making of culture and of individuals seeking support.

Some traditional healing systems focus on spirits, animal powers, or non-humans, or god-like entities (Kirmayer, 2012). Systems of healing may represent traditional forms of spirituality and world views of the social organization of the individuals. Religious considerations might include talking circles, pipe ceremonies, sweat lodges, and other culturally specific practices (Gone, 2013). For example, resiliency is built into the cultural group of the Aboriginal People of Canada; and the value is integrated into their identity, collective history, language, and spirituality (Kirmayer et al., 2011). Ultimately, cultural identity serves to improve aspects of wellness and positive feelings in oneself according to Myers and Sweeney (2008).

Other healing traditions from Latin cultures, utilize more aspects of spirituality and ritualized or indigenous practices. Body-oriented practitioners in the West explore body-mind centering, somatic experiencing, focusing, and authentic movement (Ogden et al., 2006). The sensorimotor psychotherapy approach involves the body's influences to regulate behaviors especially habitual gestures, postures, prosody, facial expressions, and eye contact. Sensorimotor psychotherapy considers the body and the somatically based symptoms of traumatized individuals as well as the cognitive and emotional processing of trauma (Ogden, 2013). This processing is an intervention that can "help regulate and facilitate emotional and cognitive processing" (Ogden & Minton, 2000, p. 150).

Connection to Creativity

An example of this experience occurred while working within the criminal justice and mental health systems in Illinois. My work on the in-patient unit required attention to aiding in mental health restorative approaches as well as returning individuals to baseline or "normative" levels prior to the criminal activities. As the expressive arts therapist on this locked unit, my role was to support adults committed to criminal activity by the judicial system. One of the struggles in this process was the language barrier and my limitations in communicating with individuals whose native language was Spanish. This barrier was overcome by utilizing an interpreter and offering a variety of native foods such as gazpacho a tomato-based Andalusian soup that is most famous for being served cold. We provided horchata, a popular Mexican drink that is often described as a sweet rice milk beverage. We chose music from the *Bueno Vista Social Club*, an ensemble of Cuban-born musicians named after a Havana members' club that closed in the 1940s.

With the doors to the activity room open, and music and food offered, the hesitant unit members filled the room. The language barrier that I had as an English speaker was minimal as we connected the clients to their traditions and cultural experiences from their past. Working with the movement therapist, we were able to engage these individuals with movements and activities that were culturally relevant and re-connected them to their cultural roots. Through the integration of sensory information and stimulation, we provided a cultural experience that offered opportunities for neural re-integration.

If we are to examine other treatment approaches that consider the body and the brain for trauma re-integration, let us turn our attention back to creativity. According to Leung et al. (2008), exposure to "multiple cultures in and of itself can enhance creativity" (p. 169). Their research indicated that there was a positive correlation between multicultural experiences and creative performance, as well as creative cognitive processes including insight learning, remote association, recruitment of new ideas, unconventional knowledge, and idea generation. This information indicates that promoting creativity may enhance global learning environments and organizational work settings.

Ethnologist, Ellen Dissanayake (1995) discussed arts and art-related activities to assist humans to return to psychological and social equilibrium. She focused on the arts as normative behaviors; as universal as the human experiences of talking, playing, and socializing. Malchiodi (2019) noted the importance of music which includes movement and sound. Music assists humans in well-being while focusing on interconnectedness, rhythm, and synchrony. She also identified other areas for well-being including storytelling which is a language-driven activity that includes ceremonies, rituals, as well as sensory-based communication. And finally, silence. The need for silence assists in quieting the human mind and regulation of the human body.

Kaiser Adverse Childhood Study

Now that we can recognize the opportunities of healing presented within creativity, let's explore the research of the long-term impact of traumatic experiences. In our knowledge of trauma and the stress response, we have learned about the long-term physical and emotional consequences of trauma from various research studies including the adverse childhood experience or ACEs studies.

From 1995 through 1997, the CDC-Kaiser Permanente Adverse Childhood Experience (ACE) Study was conducted by the U. S. health maintenance company Kaiser Permanente. It was one of the largest studies about the long-term consequences of adverse situations on children from birth to 17 years. The ACEs study revealed the impact of adverse childhood experiences of childhood abuse, neglect, witnessing violence in the home or community violence as potentially traumatic events linked to chronic health problems, mental illness, and substance misuse in adulthood (Felitti et al., 1998).

The adverse childhood experiences also included: a child experiencing a family member who attempts or dies by suicide, family members near the child dealing with substance misuse, mental health problems, or incarceration, as well as any parental separations. These experiences impact a child's environment and undermine their sense of safety and there is a prevalence of early life stress linked to the disruption of the neurodevelopmental processes and detrimentally impacting a child's wellbeing (Anderson & Finlay, 2014).

According to the American Psychological Association's (APA) Presidential Task Force on Posttraumatic Stress Disorder and Trauma in Children and Adolescents (2008), individuals who come from:

> Poverty and discrimination, racial and ethnic minority youth and families are more likely to be subjected to traumatic events, and immigrant youth and families may be particularly at risk. Cultural context and background, as well as membership in a minority group, will affect how individuals perceive a traumatic event and its impact and how the community can assist in recovery. (American Psychological Association, 2008, p. 1)

Consequences of Trauma on the Human Experience

The exposure and long-term consequences of trauma impact the client as well as the mental health clinician providing treatment. Because this exposure can be so detrimental, vernacular language has been designated for the mental health professional who is supporting the client *through* the trauma experience. The American Counseling Association has identified *vicarious trauma* (VT) as "the emotional residue of exposure that counselors have from working with people as they are hearing their trauma stories and become witness to the pain, fear, and terror that trauma survivors have endured" (American Counseling Association, 2011). The impact of the trauma experience might be so powerful to others that McCann and Pearlman (1990) acknowledged that the "therapist's cognitive world will be altered by hearing traumatic client material" (p.136). VT is unique and accumulative to counselors who engage in empathic relationships with traumatized clients (Branson, 2019).

Another clinical terminology identifies the impactful nature of trauma on those providing support to individuals who have experienced trauma. The counseling response of *countertransference* is an ideational and affective response that mental health counselors may have while working with the client or the client material (Pearlman & Saakvitne, 1995). Counselor-induced trauma response, secondary traumatic stress, compassion fatigue, and secondary victimization are similar experiences related to the vicarious trauma exposure response.

Positive Impact of Trauma Exposure

As we have noted, exposure to trauma is powerful and impactful to all individuals involved or surrounding the experience. We shall note that some of these exposures may be positive and have a strength-based influence as well. According to Groleau et al. (2012), the positive experience in the counseling session is termed post-traumatic growth [PTG]. PTG is the experience of change that does not damage despite highly stressful circumstances (Calhoun & Tedeschi, 2006). The experience of PTG is reported in five major areas that include improvement in interpersonal relationships, greater personal strengths, new opportunities, increased appreciation for life, and growth in spiritual terms. The positive experiences may impact the client's perceptions of self, interrelations with others, and create a deeper meaning for life. The positive experience for the client may also be used to describe the positive changes that occur for the mental health clinician working with the traumatized client.

Vicarious growth is another term that recognizes the positive impact of trauma work which is the act of listening to patients and looking for positive change (Calhoun & Tedeschi, 2006). The notion of vicarious growth developed out of a branch of positive psychology that explored the act of listening to patients for positive change. The qualitative study by Hernandez-Wolfe et al. (2014) found that despite the emotional pain, trauma therapists could be positively impacted by client resiliency. Themes included: observing and supporting a clients' emotional growth, spiritual growth, and resiliency. The therapist working with the traumatized client is likely to observe growth in the process and find rebirth if the counselor takes on an active role in seeking strength-based learning experiences. As mental health clinicians, we can engage more early intervention approaches to minimize the impactful damage of trauma and strengthen the resiliency factors.

As we can see, trauma exposure and environmental stressors have a tremendous impact on the individual and the collective human experience. Next, we will explore the neurobiological ramifications of the trauma experienced on the body and brain. The approach to this information is to identify the various responses that the mental health clinician may experience and determine effective treatment approaches that support emotional change and lead to psychological healing.

References for Chapter 2

Adekson, M. O. (2017). Culture and holistic healing as integral parts of indigenous global health. *JSM Health Education & Primary Health Care, 2*(2), Art. no. 1027.

American Counseling Association. (2011, October). *Vicarious trauma*. Retrieved from www.counseling.org

American Mental Health Counselors Association. (2020, May). *Code of ethics*. Retrieved from https://www.amhca.org/publications/ethics

American Psychiatric Association. (1980). *Diagnostic and statistical manual of mental disorders* (3rd ed., Text Revision). Washington, D.C: American Psychiatric Association.

American Psychiatric Association. (2000). *Diagnostic and statistical manual of mental disorders* (4th ed., Text Revision). Washington, D.C: American Psychiatric Association.

American Psychiatric Association. (2013). *Diagnostic and statistical manual of mental disorders* (5th ed.). Arlington, VA: American Psychiatric Publishing. https://doi.org/10.1176/appi.books.9780890425596

American Psychological Association. (2008). *Children andtrauma: Update for mental health professionals.* 2008 Presidential Task Force on Posttraumatic Stress Disorder and Trauma in Children and Adolescents. Retrieved from http://www.apa.org/pi/families/resources/update.pdf

American Psychological Association. (2013). Stress: The different kinds of stress. Retrieved from www.apa.org

Anderson M. L., & Finlay B. L. (2014). Allocating structure to function: The strong links between neuroplasticity and natural selection. *Frontiers in Human Neuroscience, 7*(918) 1–16.

Archibald, L. & Dewar, J. (2010). Creative arts, culture, and healing: building an evidence base 1. *Pimatiwiskin: A Journal of Aboriginal and Indigenous Community Health,* 1–26.

Beeson, E. T., & Field, T. A. (2017). Neurocounseling: A new section of the Journal of Mental Health Counseling. *Journal of Mental Health Counseling, 39,* 71–83.

Bhugra, D., & Becker, M. A. (2005). Migration, cultural bereavement, and cultural identity. *World Psychiatry, 4*(1), 18–24.

Bicknell-Hentges, L., & Lynch, J. J. (2009, March). *Everything counselors and supervisors need to know about treating trauma.* Paper based on a presentation at the American Counseling Association Annual Conference and Exposition, Charlotte, NC.

Branson, D. C. (2019). Vicarious trauma, themes in research, and terminology: A review of the literature. *Traumatology, 25*(1), 2–10. https://doi.org/10.1037/trm0000161

Briere, J., & Scott, C. (2006). *Principles of trauma therapy: A guide to symptoms, evaluation, and treatment.* Sage Publications.

Calhoun, L. G., & Tedeschi, R. G. (2006). *Expert companions: Posttraumatic growth in clinical practice.* Lawrence Erlbaum Associates Publishers.

Cameron L. (2010). Using the arts as a therapeutic tool for counselling–An Australian Aboriginal perspective. *Procedia - Social and Behavioral Sciences 5,* 403–407. DOI: 10.1016/j.sbspro.2010.07.112

Capuzzi, D., & Stauffer, M. D. (2016). *Counseling and psychotherapy.* Theories and Interventions (6th ed.). American Counseling Association.

Center for Disease Control (CDC). (2020). Global Covid-19. [retrieved on 2020, December 30]. https://www.cdc.gov/coronavirus/2019-ncov/global-covid-19/index.html

Center for Disease Control (CDC). (2020). Injury prevention. [retrieved on 2020, October 1]. https://www.cdc.gov/injury/index.html

Council for Accreditation of Counseling and Related Educational Programs. (2009). *2009 standards.* Retrieved from http://www.cacrep.org/doc/2009%20Standards.pdf

Courtois, C. A., & Gold, S. N. (2009). The need for inclusion of psychological trauma in the professional curriculum: A call to action. *Psychological Trauma: Theory, Research, Practice, and Policy, 1,* 3–23.

COVID-19 Treatment Guidelines Panel. (2019). Coronavirus Disease 2019 (COVID-19) Treatment Guidelines. National Institutes of Health. Available at https://www.covid19treatmentguidelines.nih.gov/. Accessed [2021, February 24].

Dissanayake, E. (1995). 1994 keynote address reflecting on the past: Implications of prehistory and infancy for art therapy, *Art Therapy, 12*(1), 17–23, https://doi.org/10.1080/07421656.1995.10759119

Ejaz, H., Alsrhani, A., Zafar, A., Javed, H., Junaid, K., Abdalla, A. E., Abosalif, K., Ahmed, Z., & Younas, S. (2020). COVID-19 and comorbidities: Deleterious impact on infected patients. *Journal of Infection and Public Health, 13*(12), 1833–1839, https://doi.org/10.1016/j.jiph.2020.07.014

Felitti, V. J., Anda, R. F., Nordenberg, D., Williamson, D. F., Spitz, A. M., Edwards, V., Koss, M. P., & Marks, J. S. (1998). Relationship of childhood abuse and household dysfunction to many of the leading causes of death in adults: The Adverse Childhood Experiences (ACE) Study. *American Journal of Preventive Medicine, 14*(4), 245–258. https://doi.org/10.1016/S0749-3797(98)00017-8

Gone, J. P. (2013). Redressing First Nations historical trauma: theorizing mechanisms for indigenous culture as mental health treatment. *Transcult Psychiatry, 50*(5), 683–706.

Groleau, J., Calhoun, L. G., Cann, A., & Tedeschi, R. G. (2012). The role of centrality of events in posttraumatic distress and posttraumatic growth. *Psychological Trauma: Theory, Research, Practice, and Policy*, 1–7.

Guan, W. J., Liang, W. H., Zhao, Y., Liang, H. R., Chen, Z. S., Li, Y. M.... , & Ou, C. Q. (2020). Comorbidity and its impact on 1590 patients with Covid-19 in China: A nationwide analysis. *European Respiratory Journal, 55*(5), e2000547.

Hechanova, R., & Waelde, L. (2017). The influence of culture on disaster mental health and psychosocial support interventions in Southeast Asia. *Mental Health Religion, 20*, 31–44. DOI: 10.1080/13674676.2017.1322048

Hernandez-Wolfe, P., Killian, K., Engstrom, D., & Gangsei, D. (2014, May). Vicarious resilience, vicarious trauma, and awareness of equity in trauma work. *Journal of Humanistic Psychology, 55*(2), 153–172. DOI: 10.1177/0022167814534322

Horowitz, M. (1978). *Stress response syndromes*. Jason Aronson.

Huss, E., & Cwikel, J. (2005). Researching creations: Applying arts-based research to Bedouin women's drawings Ephrat Huss and Julie Cwikel. *International Journal of Qualitative Methods, 4*, 44–62. DOI: 10.1177/160940690500400404

Insel, T., Cuthbert, B., Garvey, M., Heinssen, R., Pine, D. S., Quinn, K., Sanislow, C., & Wang, P. (2010). Research domain criteria (RDoC): Toward a new classification framework for research on mental disorders. *American Journal of Psychiatry, 167*(7), 748–751. DOI: 10.1176/appi.ajp.2010.09091379. PMID: 20595427.

Kessler, R. C., Chiu, W. T., Demler, O., Merikangas, K. R., & Walters E. E. (2005). Prevalence, severity, and comorbidity of 12-month DSM-IV disorders in the National Comorbidity Survey Replication. *Archives of General Psychiatry, 62*(7), Art. no. 709.

Kirmayer, L. J. (2012). Cultural competence and evidence-based practice in mental health: Epistemic communities and the politics of pluralism. *Social Science & Medicine, 75*, 249–256.

Kirmayer, L. J., Dandeneau, S., Marshall, E., Phillips, M. K., & Williamson, K. J. (2011). Rethinking resilience from indigenous perspectives. *Canadian Journal of Psychiatry*, *56*(2), 84–91.

Kirmayer, L., Simpson, C., & Cargo, M. (2003). Healing traditions: Culture, community and mental health promotion with canadian aboriginal peoples. *Australasian Psychiatry*, *11*(1_suppl), S15–S23. https://doi.org/10.1046/j.103 8-5282.2003.02010.x

Kluft, R. P., Bloom, S. L., & Kinzie, J. D. (2000). Treating the traumatized patient and victims of violence. In C. C. Bell (Ed.), *Psychiatric aspects of violence: Issues in prevention and treatment* (pp. 79–102).

Leung, A. K., Maddux, W. W., Galinsky, A. D., & Chiu, C. (2008). Multicultural experience enhances creativity: The when and how. *American Psychologist*, *63*(3), 169–181.

Luke, C., Miller, R., & McAuliffe, G. (2019). Neuro-informed Mental Health Counseling: A person-first perspective. *Journal of Mental Health Counseling*, *41*(1), 65–79. https://doi.org/10.17744/mehc.41.1.06

Malchiodi, C. A. (2019). *Expressive arts as healing engagement*. Keynote Presentation was given at the 30th International Trauma Conference, Seaport World Trade Center, Boston MA on June 1st, 2019.

McCann, I. L., & Pearlman, L. A. (1990). Vicarious traumatization: A framework for understanding the psychological effects of working with victims. *Journal of Traumatic Stress*, *3*(1), 131–149.

Merikangas, Kathleen R. (2005). Prevalence, severity, and comorbidity of 12-month DSM-IV disorders in the National Comorbidity Survey Replication. *Archives of General Psychiatry*, *62*(6), 617–627. DOI: 10.1001/archpsyc.62.6.617

Mukhtar, S. (2020). Pakistanis' mental health during the COVID-19. *Asian Journal of Psychiatry*, *51*, Art. no. 102127. https://doi.org/10.1016/j.ajp.2020.1 02127

Myer, J. E., & Sweeney, T. J. (2008). Wellness counseling: The evidence bases for practice. *Journal of Counseling and Development*, *86*, 482–493.

National Institute of Mental Health (NIMH). (2013). What is post-traumatic stress disorder (PTSD)? Retrieved from http://www.nimh.nih.gov/about/index.shtml

Office of the Surgeon General (US), Center for Mental Health Services (US), & National Institute of Mental Health (US). (2001 August). *Mental health: Culture, Race, and ethnicity: A supplement to mental health: A report of the surgeon general.* Rockville (MD): Substance Abuse and Mental Health Services Administration (US). Available from: https://www.ncbi.nlm.nih.gov/books/NBK44243/

Ogden, P. (2013). *Building the body's resources: Why focusing on the present moment can help us heal trauma* (webinar). National Institute for the Clinical Application of Behavioral Medicine Webinar Series. Retrieved from www.nicabm.com/training

Ogden, P., & Minton, K. (2000). Sensorimotor psychotherapy: One method for processing traumatic memory. *Traumatology*, *3*(3), 149–173.

Ogden, P., Minton, K., & Pain, C. (2006). *Trauma and the body: A sensorimotor approach to psychotherapy*. New York: W. W. Norton.

Pakpour, A. H., & Griffiths, M. D. (2020). The fear of COVID-19 and its role in preventive behaviors. *Journal of Concurrent Disorders*, *2*(1), 58–63.

Pearlman, L. A., & Saakvitne, K. W. (1995). *Trauma and the Therapist: Counter-transference and vicarious traumatization in psychotherapy with incest survivors.* New York: W. W. Norton.

Siegel, D. (2013). *Brainstorm.* New York: Penguin Publishing.

Smith, J. A. (2004). Reflecting on the development of interpretative phenomen-ological analysis and its contribution to qualitative research in psychology. *Qualitative Research in Psychology, 1*(1), 39–54.

Stein, D. J., Chiu, W. T., Hwang, I., Kessler, R. C., Sampson, N., Alonso, J., ... &Florescu, S. (2010). Cross-national analysis of the associations between traumatic events and suicidal behavior: Findings from the WHO World Mental Health Surveys. *PloS One, 5*(5), Art. no. e10574.

Sue, D. W., & Sue, D. (2013). *Counseling the culturally diverse: Theory and practice.* Hoboken, NJ: John Wiley and Sons.

Valentine, G., Sporton, D., & Nielsen, K. (2009). Identities and belonging: A study of Somali refugee and asylum seekers living in the UK and Denmark. *Environment and Planning D-society & Space, 27*, 234–250. 10.1068/d3407.

Van der Kolk, B. A., McFarlane, A. C., & Weisaeth, L. (Eds.). (1996). *Traumatic stress: The effects of overwhelming experience on mind, body, and society.* Guilford Press.

World Health Organization (WHO). (2009). Disease and injury regional estimates for 2004. Geneva, Switzerland. Survey Replication. *Archives of General Psychiatry, 62*(6), 593–602. https://covid19.who.int/

World Health Organization (WHO). (2010). *Mental health and development: Targeting people with mental health conditions as a vulnerable group,* Geneva, WHO Press.

Yehuda, R. (1997). Sensitization of the hypothalamic-pituitary-adrenal axis in posttraumatic stress disorder. *Annals of the New York Academy of Sciences, 821*, 57–73.

Yehuda, R., & McFarlane, A. (1996). Conflict between current knowledge about posttraumatic stress disorder and its original conceptual basis. *American Journal of Psychiatry, 152* (12), 1705–1713.

3 Neurophysiology of the Human Brain and Central Nervous System

Psychodynamic Traditions of Attachment

We will begin to review the processes relevant to the traditions of psychodynamic psychotherapy and further explore the neurobiological workings of the brain. Psychodynamic psychotherapy focuses on examining the interpersonal relationship created in the counseling room between the psychotherapist and the client. The counseling relationship leads to more clarity of the client's attachment style, their early life memories and experiences, and traumas leading to subsequent internalized fears for the client.

In psychodynamic therapy, the core principles are revealed within the interpersonal relationship between the client and the psychodynamic therapist. The focus in treatment is placed on helping the clients gain insight and understanding into their lives and present-day problems. The therapeutic relationship is the primary example of how the client interacts with others. These interactional patterns are examined by reviewing the emotions, thoughts, early-life experiences, and beliefs held by the client. Through transference, an important process as the client 'transfers' their feelings for early attachment figures (maternal/paternal figures, early care caregivers, etc.) onto the therapist. This process can reveal a client's relationship patterns and may allow for awareness and empowerment to transform and alter the experiences.

Within the psychodynamic process, the client utilizes defense mechanisms that serve to protect the client from painful feelings, memories, and experiences locked in the client's unconscious mind. The psychotherapist supports the client in identifying those defense mechanisms through the conscious awareness of the fears, desires, and emotions of the client. As these unconscious thoughts and feelings are explored, the defensive mechanism is processed and can be reduced or resolved.

In reviewing the neurobiology impacted by this tradition of psychodynamic psychotherapy, we shall gain more insight into the inner working of the brain and what is necessary for creating therapeutic change in mental health. There is still much to understand within the

DOI: 10.4324/9781003030591-3

neurobiological experience of the brain during psychotherapy. In terms of memories and the process of neurobiologically altering the pathogenic memory in the psychotherapy process. At least two mechanisms of unwanted memory-erasing appear to be implicated in the effects of psychotherapy: inhibition of memory consolidation/reconsolidation and extinction.

The spinal cord runs into the brain stem and the amygdala and hippocampus are small parts of the brain that sit above the brain stem, are connected to the primitive brain. The amygdala measures the importance of emotional memories while the hippocampus stores facts. The amygdala stores the emotional memories without words, for the entire length of human life. These memories might be considered the "unconscious" and will immediately alert every part of the brain and body to act. For example, when something fear-inducing occurs, the amygdala will remind the system of something from the past and send hormones and the individual is activated for 'fight or flight.' The entire system is activated or running on autopilot and under these circumstances, the cerebrum and the neo-cortex or the higher parts of the intellectual brain, cannot mediate the response.

The process of psychotherapy serves to help people transfer information from the emotional and primitive part of the brain, the amygdala, to the frontal lobes or the prefrontal cortex for more intellectual reasoning and thought. This process reduces the responses to trauma memories and reworks the memory storage process. In memory formation and consolidation, memories can be updated, modified, and erased. For a normalized situation, the frontal lobes of the brain, control our reactions because the information is sent from the amygdala to the frontal lobes where the information is evaluated and responded to in an appropriate manner. We have time to think it over before responding.

Attachment is the emotional engagement between the client and the therapist; and the neurochemistry of attachment involves the neuropeptide oxytocin, which when mixed estrogen induces maternal behaviors of caring and attending for others. Oxytocin in humans increases feelings of trust, social learning, empathy, eye contact, generosity, and decreased anxiety (Rizzolatti et al., 1996). Ultimately the process of attachment serves to reduce the level of distress in the amygdala.

There are other processes that support neuronal changes during the psychotherapeutic process. For example, the emotional regulation process that occurs in psychotherapy is connected to the reappraisal experience of experiencing a feeling and reworking the response, which modifies brain activity. Linking cognitive control with emotional experiences enhances a client's experience, empathy, and overcoming fears leading to fear extinction. Also, mirror neurons and empathy is connected to the same premotor cortex neurons which come from maintaining the same physical 'space' with another.

Neurobiology of the Human Brain and Central Nervous System

Now, let's examine the neurophysiology of the central nervous system (CNS) and understand why survival instincts are innate. The early humans lived life for the survival of the species. This vigilance or activated state, however, comes with a hefty price. As our predecessors engaged in survival approaches to maintain the act of living, this survival approach impacts the nervous system and the human brain of today's humans.

Identify a stressful situation that has impacted you in recent days. Maybe it was a work deadline that was creating worry about your job or your future career plans. The stressful experience and excessive worry might be leading you to question your ability to put food on the table or support your family. The original worry is there to cause your system to be activated. Is your survival on the line? It might be, so you become activated to step up your work responsibilities and complete the work deadline. When the worry occurs, your nervous system is becoming primed and activated for action. However, when nervous system activation occurs, the neurophysiological response system cannot differentiate the level of severity of the survival threat.

Neurobiology of Stress

During the neurobiological response of the human *central nervous system* (CNS), the experience of stress has a dramatic effect on the physical body and the human brain. The CNS is comprised of the spinal cord which carries neuronal information and energy from the body and the central nervous system to the brain. The energy flow enters the vagal nerve into the brain stem and helps to regulate bodily function and the state of arousal. This state includes the fight, flight, and freeze reactions, and is registered and responded to as a threat or a perceived threat (Siegel, 2012). Levine (2010) discussed the ethological research that has focused on the body's response to an active threat. He describes the human immobility response of "Arrest (increased vigilance, scanning), Flight (try first to escape), Fight (if the animal or person is prevented from escaping), Freeze (fright-scared stiff), and Fold (collapse into helplessness)" (p. 48).

Central Nervous System (CNS)

The central nervous system includes the autonomic nervous system (ANS) which consists of both the sympathetic nervous system and the parasympathetic systems simultaneously. The sympathetic nervous system activates the nervous system response by drastically increasing the adrenal and cortisol levels for action. As a result, the respiration and heart rate increase rapidly which sends blood away from the skin and into the muscles, etc. The goal of the parasympathetic nervous system is to return the system back to the normal physiological activity which includes decreasing the heart rate, breathing rate, and blood flow to the digestive system.

The various states of arousal allow the system to arm and protect itself, whether by challenging the threat for survival or reducing the severity of possible mortal damage to the perceived threat (Gunnar, 2007). If the threat is imminent or prolonged, the brain can also release hormones to activate the parasympathetic branch (PNS) of the ANS, and freezing and tonic immobility can result (Gallup & Maser, 1977; van der Kolk, 1994). The stress response systems of the nervous system allow for adaptation and responsiveness to adverse circumstances (Heim et al., 2008). The body's neurochemical goal, ultimately, is to return to normal or homeostatic levels of functioning.

Neurophysiological Stress Response Vulnerability

Stress causes the body to activate its survival mechanisms, including the immune, neuroendocrine, peripheral, hypothalamic-pituitary, and neurochemical systems (Weber & Reynolds, 2004). The stress disrupts the homeostasis of the client's physical body but does not necessarily cause long-term health issues. The system allows the individual to identify and cope with the type, duration, frequency, and intensity of the stressor (Weber & Reynolds, 2004). When the system perceives stress, it releases various neurotransmitters into the brain including dopamine, norepinephrine, serotonin, and acetylcholine. This "stimulates the hypothalamus, pituitary gland, and adrenal glands, which releases cortisol" (Weber & Reynolds, 2004, p. 121). These high cortisol levels serve to activate the system but can cause brain alterations and a weaker immune system, and it can also have the opposite effect of shutting down the brain's stress response and shutting down damaging reactions to the brain's system (Yehuda, 1997).

Potential Harm

As we examine the impact, we understand that the body and brain are responding to a threat for activation and ultimately, for resolution back to homeostasis. However, repeated activation of the stress response may cause long-term effects on the body. The stress response may cause alterations in the brain that contribute to mental health issues including anxiety, depression, and addiction. By examining the various systems, we can better recognize the potential harm that stress has on the neurophysiological nervous system. At this point, we should better understand the human endocrine system.

Endocrine System

The endocrine system and the related glands and organs of the body produce hormones that regulate aspects of mood, metabolism, response to injury and stress, energy levels, growth and development, and tissue function. The hypothalamus is located at the base of the brain and secretes hormones that stimulate or suppress hormonal release in the pituitary gland and controls water balance, sleep, temperature, appetite, and blood pressure. Cortisol is the steroid hormone that is released during the experience of stress. The impact of cortisol on the body's immune system may leave it weakened thus allowing the body to more vulnerable to infection, colds, flu, and certain types of cancer (American Psychological Association [APA], 2012). Further research is needed to determine what impact stress may have on specific types of cancer. Prolonged elevations of cortisol levels may increase the risk of disease and of neuronal death in the hippocampus.

The physical response to repeated trauma exposure includes elevated levels of adrenaline, a hormone that is present in the bloodstream. This hormone increases cholesterol production, which decreases the rate at which cholesterol is removed from the bloodstream and increases the deposits of plaque on the arterial walls. These conditions increase the risk of experiencing stroke and heart disease.

The body's endorphin levels assist in natural pain relief and lowering of the endorphins can decrease the sense of well-being that is typically produced by the presence of those endorphins. This can lead to increased arthritis pain and severe headaches. Low endorphin levels may also contribute to the use of various drugs such as caffeine and other substances, to increase or mimic the effects of well-being (APA, 2012).

The change in the body's circulation may increase the risk of high blood pressure and migraine headaches. Also, an increased level of acid production in the stomach increases the risk of experiencing chronic stomach and digestive upsets causing diarrhea, constipation, cramping, and bloating (APA, 2012).

The Limbic System

The limbic system is the emotional center of the brain and controls our behaviors and emotional responses related to survival, feeding, reproduction, and our fight or flight responses. The limbic system includes the amygdala, hippocampus, thalamus, hypothalamus, basal ganglia, and cingulate gyrus. Once the brain systems recognize the stressors, the limbic system activates the emotions essential for survival under perceived stress (Van der Kolk, 1993). The limbic system shows abnormalities in the arousal mechanisms of the sympathetic nervous system after severe trauma exposure. Our central stress response system is the hypothalamic-pituitary-adrenal (HPA) axis and connects the central nervous system with the endocrine system. These connections activate the stress systems even before the visual center of the brain becoming aware of what is happening. Our bodies may respond before our brain is cognizant of highly stressful situations, such as a speeding car coming towards you and your body automatically jumps out of the way.

The hippocampus consists of several structures that are active in the process of emotion and memory (Solms & Turnbull, 2002, p. 17). The episodic memories are formed and filed for long-term memory storage. The amygdala controls our emotional response to fear, pleasure, anxiety, and anger. Repeatedly encountering terrifying or life-threatening events can desensitize the amygdala. It can take less and less emotion to activate the amygdala causing the individual to feel chronically alert and jumpy after exposure to trauma.

Over-activation of the hippocampus can occur while under high emotional stress or trauma leading to the deactivation of the hippo-campus. Due to consistently high levels of glucocorticoids, a hormone steroid, that causes the cells in the hippocampus to shrink. This can also compromise the brain's ability to establish and consolidate new memories (Conrad, 2008). The occurrence of the hippocampus deactivation can indicate neuronal damage and plays a critical role in the development of anxiety and panic disorders (Rappaport, 2014).

Protective Neuronal Factors

We have explored various negative impactful experiences of stress on the system. Our intention in this discussion is to seek out strength-based or protective factors to support the trauma experience. In terms of the neuronal response to stress, it is noted in the research that there are positive factors such as resilience that may protect the client. In the neurophysiological experiences of trauma and neuronal responses, re-siliency might offer some relief. Resiliency is connected to the rapid ac-tivation and efficient release of the stress response and is thought to include an optimal balance of the glucocorticoid and mineralocorticoid receptor functions within the Hypothalamic-Pituitary-Adrenal (HPA) system (Charney, 2004).

As we note, the body's neurochemical goal is to return to normal levels of functioning. Dehydroepiandrosterone (DHEA) is an adrenal steroid released with cortisol that may increase stress resistance by protecting against neural damage from the HPA activity. Feder et al. (2010) explain how it counteracts corticosteroid neurotoxicity in the hippocampus (2010). The blockage of beta-adrenergic receptors in the amygdala can decrease the development of negative memories. Also, dopamine neurons are activated by rewarding stimuli and delaying negative stimuli. This process may be a critical component in stress protection on mood and well-being (Luthar & Cicchetti, 2000).

Neuronal Activity and Neuroplasticity

The human brain has over 100 billion neurons that are responsible for receiving sensory input from the external world, transforming and relaying the electrical signals, and sending motor commands to the muscles. Another cellular response is called *neuroplasticity* and is a dynamic neuronal response to an environment that gradually alters cellular structure and function. The process of *neuroplasticity* is the alteration of neuronal firings that are impacted by the real-life experiences occurring around the individual. New neurons are made in the hippocampus and the brain region may show neuronal growth or *neurogenesis*. With the process of neuronal activation, Scaer (2012) examines how the *neurons that fire together, wire together* and with "enhanced learning and skill acquisition and shrinkage with emotional illness and physical disease of the brain" (p. 2). The brain is impacted by environmental stressors and this process occurs at a "neuronal level and reveals how the activation of neurons firing can be altered" (Siegel, 2012, p. 3–4).

The Role of Specific Brain Systems

The basal ganglia are a set of neural structures or clusters of nerve cells inside the cerebrum that process information from different regions of the cerebral cortex. Information is then returned to the motor cortex allowing for well-coordinated voluntary movements. The prefrontal cortex controls the executive functions of the brain and is responsible for attention, working memory, integration of motor and speech activity with sensory information (Rappaport, 2014). There can be changes in behavior that stress can impact hemisphere integration which could lead to psychopathology (Teicher et al., 1997).

The human brain has some fail-safe approaches to protecting the neural physiological system. The specific brain systems provide opportunities for protection of the harmful impacts of the stress response on the neural system. In some cases, the corpus callosum may not share hemispheric information between both sides of the brain. This protective measure supports the various brain systems from becoming overwhelmed by highly stressful material. It is speculated that stress can impact hemisphere integration which could lead to psychopathology (Teicher et al., 1997). It is also believed that neuronal information is transported to the cortex and the mid-prefrontal cortex regions of the brain and the anterior cingulate coordinates the bodily response to the information with more attention and emotion. Within the prefrontal region, decision-making strategies may demonstrate a shift from flexible behavior to ones dominated by positive or negative habits. This may be the point where resilient behaviors become engaged or where impulsive or even dangerous behaviors become integrated into the client's behavioral system.

Long Term Consequences

Stress plays a crucial role in the pathogenesis, onset, and progression of various illnesses. In turn, numerous somatic, as well as psychiatric diseases, come along with altered HPA axis responses to acute stress (Chrousos, 2009). When the body has been activated by stress, long-term exposure, or the inability to effectively deal with the exposure to stress, the chances of long-term health concerns increase. The stress system becomes maladaptive if the compensatory stress response is fatigued and cannot return to pre-stress homeostasis levels thus resulting in alterations of the brain's structure and functioning levels. PTSD patients in the community maintain high incidents of medical conditions that may include health issues related to hypertensive and metabolic concerns.

Sareen 2007 Long-term consequences for the exposure to trauma indicate high levels of physical and mental health considerations. In fact, "asthma, chronic obstructive pulmonary disease, chronic fatigue syndrome, arthritis, fibromyalgia, migraine headaches, cancer, and other respiratory, cardiovascular, gastrointestinal, or pain disorders" (Sareen et al., 2007, p. 242).

The literature shows early life stress may alter the development and functioning of the stress response system that lasts into adulthood. Stressful environments resulting in reoccurring states of alarm could become more trait-like as those connections relevant to arousal are activated and those underlying typical developmental states are more subject to synaptic elimination. Complex neuroactivities are processed through multiple hierarchies of neurocircuits and may have different periods of development sensitivity that are prone to axonal elaboration, synaptic elimination, or synaptic consolidation (Zeanah, 2009).

Allostasis

As we have stated, the body's neurochemical goal is to return to normal levels of functioning. The term *allostasis* named by Sterling and Eyer (1988). As we have stated, the body's neurochemical goal is to return to normal levels of functioning. The term allostasis named by Sterling and Eyer (1988) describes the body's process of adapting to stressors to return to homeostasis. The process of maintaining homeostasis through the adaptive alteration of the organism's internal environment to meet the perceived demands. For example, the trauma experience can overpower an individual's resources so treatment goals will need to be tailored to activities that restore the balance between resources and trauma (Ellis &

Del Giudice, 2014). As mental health clinicians, treatment approaches include supporting the client where they are at in the trauma experience and providing opportunities to assist the client in returning to homeostasis. These stress reduction techniques serve the client in learning to reduce the stress response and returning to a homeostatic baseline.

References

American Psychological Association. (2012). *Stress in America - American Psychological Association* [Received on 3 January 2020]. https://www.apa.org/news/press/releases/stress/2011/final-2011.pdf

Charney, D. S. (2004). Psychobiological mechanisms of resilience and vulnerability: Implications for adaptation to extreme stress. *American Journal of Psychiatry, 161*, 195–216.

Chrousos, G. (2009). Stress and disorders of the stress system. *Nature Reviews Endocrinology 5*, 374–381. https://doi.org/10.1038/nrendo.2009.106

Conrad C. D. (2008). Chronic stress-induced hippocampal vulnerability: the glucocorticoid vulnerability hypothesis. *Reviews in the Neurosciences, 19*(6), 395–411.

Ellis, B., & Del Giudice, M. (2014). Beyond allostatic load: Rethinking the role of stress in regulating human development. *Development and Psychopathology, 26*(1), 1–20. DOI: 10.1017/S0954579413000849

Feder, A., Nestle, E. J., Westphal, M., & Charney, D. S. (2010). Psychobiological mechanisms of resilience to stress. In J. W. Reich, A. J. Zautra, & J. S. Hall (Eds.), *Handbook of adult resilience* (pp. 35–54). New York: Guilford Press.

Gallup, G. G., Jr., & Maser, J. D. (1977). Catatonia: Tonic immobility: Evolutionary underpinnings of human catalepsy and catatonia. In J. D. Maser & M. E. P. Seligman (Eds.), *A series of books in psychology. Psychopathology: Experimental models* (pp. 334–357). W H Freeman/Times Books/ Henry Holt & Co.

Gunnar, M. R. (2007). Stress effects on the developing brain. In D. Romer & E. F. Walker (Eds.), *Adolescent psychopathology and the developing brain: Integrating brain and prevention science* (pp. 127–147). Oxford University Press. https://doi.org/10.1093/acprof

Heim, C., Newport, D. J., Mletzko, T., Miller, A. H., & Nemeroff, C. B. (2008). The link between childhood trauma and depression: Insights from HPA axis studies in humans. *Psychoneuroendocrinology, 33*(6), 693-710. https://doi.org/10.1016/j.psyneuen.2008.03.008

Lang, P. J., & Bradley, M. M. (2010). Emotion and the motivational brain. *Biological Psychology, 84*(3), 437–450. https://doi.org/10.1016/j.biopsycho.2009.10.007

Levine, P. A. (2010). *In an unspoken voice: How the body releases trauma and restores goodness.* Berkeley, CA: North Atlantic Books.

Luthar, S. S., & Cicchetti, D. (2000). The construct of resilience: Implications for interventions and social policies. *NIHPA Author Manuscripts, 12*(4), 1–32.

McEwen, G., & Gianaros, P. (2011). Stress- and allostasis-induced brain plasticity. *Annual Review of Medicine, 62*(1), 431–445. https://doi.org/10.1146/annurev-med-052209-100430

Rappaport, L. (Ed.). (2014). *Mindfulness and the arts therapies: Theory and practice.* London: Jessica Kingsley Publishers.

Rizzolatti, G., Fadiga, L., Gallese, V., & Fogassi, L. (1996). Premotor cortex and the recognition of motor actions. *Cognitive Brain Research, 3,* 131–141.

Sareen, J., Cox, B. J., Stein, M. B., Afifi, T. O., Fleet, C., & Asmundson, G. J. (2007). Physical and mental comorbidity, disability, and suicidal behavior associated with posttraumatic stress disorder in a large community sample. *Psychosomatic Medicine, 69*(3), 242–248.

Scaer, R. (2012). *Eight keys to brain-body balance.* New York: W. W. Norton.

Segerstrom, S. C., & Miller, G. E. (2004). Psychological stress and the human immune system: a meta-analytic study of 30 years of inquiry. *Psychological Bulletin, 130*(4), 601–630. https://doi.org/10.1037/0033-2909.130.4.601

Siegel, D. (2012). *Pocket guide to interpersonal neurobiology* (vol. 21, pp. 349–356). New York: W. W. Norton.

Solms, M., & Turnbull, O. (2002). *The brain and the inner world: An introduction to the neuroscience of subjective experience.* New York: Other Press.

Sterling, P., & Eyer, J. (1988). Allostasis, a new paradigm to explain arousal pathology. I. S. Fisher & J. Reason (Eds.), *Handbook of life stress, cognition, and health* (pp. 629–649). New York: Wiley.

Teicher, M., Ito, Y., Glod, C. A., Andersen, S. L., Dumont, N., & Ackerman, E. (1997). Preliminary evidence for abnormal cortical development in physically and sexually abused children using EEG coherence and MRI. *Annals of New York Academy of Sciences, 821,* 160–175.

Van der Kolk, B. (1993). *Biological considerations about emotions, trauma, memory, and the brain.* In S. L. Ablon, D. Brown, E. J. Khantzian, & J. E. Mack (Eds.), *Human feelings: Explorations in affect development and meanings.* Analytic Press: Hillsdale, NJ.

van der Kolk, B. A. (1994). The body keeps the score: Memory and the evolving psychobiology of posttraumatic stress. *Harvard Review of Psychiatry, 1*(5), 253–265. DOI: 10.3109/10673229409017088

Weber, D. A., & Reynolds, C. R. (2004). Clinical perspectives on neurobiological effects of psychological trauma. *Neuropsychology Review, 14*(2), 115–129.

Yehuda, R. (1997). Sensitization of the hypothalamic-pituitary-adrenal axis in posttraumatic stress disorder. *Annals of the New York Academy of Sciences, 821,* 57–73.

Zeanah, C. H. (2009). The Importance of early experiences: Clinical, research, and policy perspectives, *Journal of Loss and Trauma, 14*(4), 266–279, DOI: 10.1080/15325020903004426

4 Clinical Mental Health Stress Reduction Techniques

There are various psychotherapeutic methods that have been proven effective in the process of stress reduction. These techniques focus on self-regulation through mindful practice and cultivating body and breath awareness through intentionality. The first technique is the Stress Inoculation Training (SIT) originally developed by Meichenbaum (1985) which supports the concept of *inoculation* and offers protection prior to the experience of stress. This training teaches coping skills and utilizes various techniques such as deep muscle relaxation, cognitive restructuring, breathing exercises, assertiveness skills, thought stopping, role-playing, and guided self-dialogue.

Spirituality

Spirituality is a highly important protective factor found within the research regarding health and wellness. Myers and Sweeney (2008) identified spirituality within the "Wheel of Wellness" as the "most important characteristic of wellbeing" (p. 483) which involves creating a personal sense of life's meaning, as well as religious and spiritual understanding. Although the research is limited on this concept, cumulative reviews of spiritual issues have found protective factors of spirituality related to health. Simpson and Starkey stated that spirituality provides a source of "hope, meaning, and purpose, particularly during difficult times" (Simpson & Starkey, 2006, p. 3). Spirituality includes the conceptual attitudes and beliefs of wellness and mindfulness, whether it is in the universal area of religion, or on a personal and individualized basis, and is considered vital to the holistic wellness of an individual (Cashwell et al., 2007).

Self-regulation is another protective stress reduction technique that includes the act of being mindful. Being mindful requires a process called metacognition, or awareness of knowledge or observing thoughts that individuals may have (Allen et al., 2006). The role of self-regulation is a core value of belief for this meditative or mindfulness approach. The incorporation of the mindfulness techniques leads the individual to a proactive method of reducing the central nervous systems' stress activation

DOI: 10.4324/9781003030591-4

system. The goal with mindfulness approaches seeks to increase bodily awareness and reflective learning within the body. And by doing so, the client can proactively train their system to reduce activation. Ultimately, the use of mindfulness techniques "can potentially teach greater self-awareness, increased impulse control, and decreased reactivity to difficult events" (Thompson & Gauntlett-Gilbert, 2008, p. 396).

Intention breathwork is a critical component to stress reduction and bodily self-awareness. With intentional breathwork, the client concentrates on self-awareness of their breath and breathing and focuses on reducing systematic activation. Intentional breath work reduces the body's bodily responses to stress and aids in the physiological feeling of calm and relaxation. Also, of importance involves paying attention to the thoughts that come into cognition and allowing those thoughts to enter the brain and exit without judgment. The client makes the decision to allow positive thoughts to enter and stay while letting negative thoughts exit the mind. This way of thinking empowers the client to non-judgmentally build control of their thoughts and their thinking process as well as their bodily stress system.

Mindful Examination

The purpose of this mindful examination is to recognize the neurophysiological impact that mindfulness may have on the client's body and brain while working towards a decrease in the overall negative stress response. As mental health clinicians, the focus in the counseling session is placed on the client gaining self-awareness and insight into their individualized neuro-typical responses to stress. Mindfulness in the counseling session may be an effective approach towards strengthening the client's emotional core and building resiliency levels into the neurophysiological responses of the brain, as well as enhancing the client's emotional protective factors to better handle future levels of stress.

For the past thirty years, the western approach led by Jon Kabat-Zinn has focused on the use of mindfulness-based stress reduction (MBSR) (Kabat-Zinn, 1994, 2009). An eight-week evidence-based program that deals with stress, anxiety, depression, and pain reduction through inviting cultivation and sustaining attention in particular ways. Kabat-Zinn's definition thus indicates that mindfulness involves (a) self-regulation of one's awareness, (b) directing one's attention to internal and external stimuli, (c) introspection and metacognitive awareness of one's thoughts processes, and (d) adopting a nonjudgmental attitude (Bishop et al., 2004). Kabat-Zinn (2009) "mindfulness is the aim, the methods or practices, and the outcome or consequences all wrapped up together" (p. xxix). The mindfulness model comprises three consistent elements that include intention and knowing why we practice mindfulness and understanding the motivation for it. Next, attention and observing the operations from moment to moment and internal and external experience, and finally, the attitude and the quality one brings to attention (Jankowski & Holas, 2014; Shapiro & Carlson, 2009).

Meditative Mindfulness

Mindfulness originates as Buddhist meditation and involves contemplative traditions growing from Eastern philosophical wisdom and teachings. Mindfulness has been defined as "paying attention in a particular way: on purpose, in the present moment, and non-judgmentally" (Kabat-Zinn, 1994, p. 8). Mindfulness maintains a phenomenological quality with spiritual and religious overtones and has been more recently translated into the realm of Western psychology and health care (Shapiro, 2009). From the Buddhism concept, mindfulness is described as a "means of enhancing attentional stability and clarity and using these abilities in the introspective examination of conscious states to pursue the fundamental issues concerning consciousness itself" (Wallace, 2005, p. 5). Understanding the history of mindfulness will better prepare us for the act of being mindful and in engaging in the process.

History of Mindfulness

The word mindfulness originally comes from Pali, the language of the scriptures of the Theravada school of Buddhism. The English word for mindfulness is *sati* which equates to having awareness, attention and remembering (Bodhi, 2000). Mindfulness involves intentionality with current thoughts and "captures a quality of consciousness that is characterized by clarity and vividness of current experience and functioning" (Brown & Ryan, 2003, p. 823). It is an act that allows one to disengage from automatic thoughts and behaviors for the purpose of reducing unhealthy patterns of behaviors.

The mindfulness approach originated with Gautama Buddha, born Prince Siddhartha about 2,600 years ago. The core message of this approach by Buddha and the Eastern traditions is to "be mindful" (Thera, 1996, p. 23). Buddha explored the Eightfold Path for the reduction in suffering and increased awareness in life. The eightfold path gives an individual the strategies for the reduction of pain caused by the conditions in living life. This path represents the guidelines on how to improve life situations and it involves active participation in maintaining decent behaviors through right viewpoints, right intention, right speech, right action, right livelihood, right effort, right meditation, and right mindfulness (Bodhi, 1998).

Meditation and Asceticism

Many religious practices have maintained some form of spirituality and enlightenment through meditation and asceticism. However, there is a struggle in naming the experience. As a result, different terms may represent a similar construct. For example, aspects of Hinduism regularly practice the cultivation of mindfulness approaches such as yoga and asceticism. The religious beliefs of Christians maintain similar practices of contemplative, ritualized prayer, and meditation within their religious activities. Judaism teachings are guided by the "Kavanah" of intention and flow of consciousness which resides in the soul, while Islamic beliefs bring awareness and non-judgmental focus into the present moment of time.

Spiritual or Secular

Mindfulness practices can be learned through the spiritual or the secular settings and require formal or informal practices towards enlightenment. Many of these holistic beliefs resemble basic concepts of mindfulness which include meditation and mindful awareness. Cultivating a mindfulness-based approach provides a holistic activity that encourages non-judgmental awareness of the current moment in time, with intentionally attending in an open, caring, and discerning way while accepting thoughts without attaching emotion (Kabat-Zinn, 1994).

Neuronal Activity During Mindfulness

Mindfulness is a powerful tool in the clinical mental health setting as it empowers the individual to gain control over their thoughts, feeling, and behaviors without medical intervention and with limited guidance. The practice supports the active observation of habituated thought patterns and emotions and expands its roots to an observational technique. Noticing the present moment fully with our ingrained five senses, to take in the sights, smells, sounds, tastes, and sensations that occur in real-time without judgment towards ourselves or towards the environment.

The act of mindfulness serves as a teaching method to assist individuals in learning to relieve human suffering, increase human compassion, and help with the act of enlightenment (Kabat-Zinn, 2003). Mindful awareness results in neuronal activity and growth in the human brain by focusing attention on the act of intention. By doing so, the axonal fibers at the prefrontal region engage other areas of the brain including the cortex, limbic area, body, brainstem, and the social world of others (Siegel, 2007). Mindful activities such as the body scan, involve placing focus and concentration on the internal feelings within the body. The scan begins at the top of the head and the mind and slowly proceeds down the spinal column. As the scan moves downward, the client feels the internal fluids slowly moving to pay special attention to areas of tightness such as tension in the shoulders or tightness in the neck.

Clinical psychology owes much to Buddhism for the creation of mindfulness and mindfulness as practiced in therapy sessions; though far removed from these beginnings, mindfulness has helped clients make remarkable progress in therapy. Mindfulness as an intervention has gained strong empirical support throughout the field of clinical psychology, and its presence in this field continues to flourish. According to Kostanski and Hassed (2008), Kabat-Zinn's (1990) initial application of mindfulness also led to popular third-wave cognitive-behavioral therapeutic practices that are used today with millions of clients, namely Dialectical Behavioral Therapy (DBT) and Acceptance and Commitment Therapy (ACT) (Kabat-Zinn, 2003). ACT has six core principles rooted in mindfulness including present moment, values, committed action, self as context, defusing, and finally, acceptance (Hayes & Smith, 2005).

Mindfulness Research

Stress reduction positively affects the efficacy of stress regulation by improving the ability to concentrate (Sedlmeier et al., 2012), decreases the fear of being judged, as well as reduces aversive self-conscious experiences (Brown et al., 2007), and helps to deal with thoughts and feelings (Shapiro et al., 2006). Evidence-based research has shown that mindfulness decreases depression, anxiety, and diverse stress-related disorders according to Brown and Ryan (2003). Brain structure research conducted by Lazar et al. (2005) suggested that meditation may be associated with structural changes in areas of the brain that are important for sensory, cognitive, and emotional processing. The data further suggests that meditation may impact age-related declines in cortical structure. Other research has found mindfulness interventions served to lessen the severity of psychological disorders such as rumination, neuroticism, stress, and anxiety (Baer, 2003; Keng et al., 2011; Chiesa & Serretti, 2009, 2010; Grossman et al., 2004).

Positive Psychology

A significant correlation between mindfulness and positive affect, life satisfaction, and an overall sense of well-being has led to the development of a new positivistic psychology orientation. Positive Psychology was developed in the 1990s and is a theoretical orientation or scientific study that considers positive thinking as a tool for general physical and mental health (Seligman, 2002).

The Positive Psychology movement focuses on the utilization of mindfulness. With the connection to cultivating positive emotion, the individual can create the experience that they are seeking. Those moments may be felt in a positive, negative, or neutral way by the individual however, it must include the simple acceptance of the feeling without the emotion. Other key concepts include empathy, happiness, gratitude, meaning, and flow and serve to strengthen virtues and "buffer against misfortune and against the psychological disorders, and [they] may be the key to building resilience" (Seligman, 2002, p. xii). The three main pillars for guidance include the study of positive emotion, positive traits along with strength and virtue, and positive institutions (such as democracy, family, and free inquiry).

As we can see, strengthening an individual's coping strategies can be beneficial to reducing the impact of trauma exposure. Mindfulness and intentional positive thinking approaches such as focus, grounding, listening, and self-reflection are effective in building trauma resiliency. The act of meditation and creativity allows for cognitive flexibility that supports healing from trauma according to the research of positive and impactful strengthening techniques. The enhancement of mindfulness through practicing meditation (Lutz et al., 2007) as well as a high level of self-reported mindfulness have previously been linked to processes important to creativity (Colzato et al., 2012).

Definition of Creativity

Creativity is the ability to produce ideas that are both novel and appropriate (Amabile, 1996; Sternberg & Lubart, 1996). A wide body of research has shown that meditation training enhances creative thinking and creative performance as well as improves the ability to solve insight problems (Colzato et al., 2012; Ding et al., 2014, 2015; Ostafin & Kassman, 2012; Ren et al., 2011). Meditative training facilitates creative elaboration (Zabelina et al., 2011) and experienced meditators outperform others in verbal fluency and are better at finding novel solutions to a given problem (Greenberg et al., 2012). Importantly, meditation has a positive effect on creativity regardless of the length of practice (Jedrczak et al., 1985), which means that even short meditation can effectively stimulate creative abilities (Ding et al., 2014).

Creativity and Mindfulness

In integrating the processes of mindfulness and creativity, researchers have found personality trait approaches that positively support the traumatized client. Several abilities are associated with trait mindfulness or facilitated by mindfulness training which is linked with creativity (De Dreu et al., 2012). For instance, mindfulness is associated with the increased ability to switch perspectives (Carson & Langer, 2006; Feldman et al., 2007), while mindfulness training leads to the improvement of working memory (Chiesa et al., 2011), as well as increases the ability to respond in a non-habitual fashion (Moore & Malinowski, 2009). Practicing mindfulness also reduces the fear of judgment (Carson & Langer, 2006), which is conducive to creativity (Baas et al., 2008; Nijstad et al., 2010). Consequently, mindfulness maybe both, directly and indirectly, related to creative thinking (Davis, 2009, De Dreu et al., 2008), and to creative achievement (Langer, 2014).

The Construct of Creativity and Strength

Neurocognitive research on creativity is at a very early stage of understanding. Definitions of creativity and models of cognitive problem-solving, new idea generation, and clarity in the processes connected to making art have no clear consensus. As we dive deeper into the cognitive construct of creativity, we find that many authors have various conceptualizations about how the process is effectively utilized. Creativity is considered to have three main stages according to Helmholtz (1826) which include the aspects of preparation, innovation, and creative production. Preparation requires general intelligence and specific domain knowledge and skills that allow them to discover, develop, and produce a creative product. Two major factors involve the exposure and the experience which supports the creator's ability to store, process, and utilize relevant knowledge. Incubation is a part of the stage where a person's brain unconsciously searches for an answer. Innovation requires the ability to disengage from what others may have done and honor divergent thinking which includes risk-taking, novelty-seeking, and convergent thinking. Finally, creative production is the result of engaging in the creative process.

Others creativity researchers including Bronowski (1972), considered creativity as the "ability to find unity in what appears to be diversity" according to Heilman (2016). Wallas (1926) suggested the prevalence of four stages of preparation that include the preparation of learning skills and knowledge to produce a creative product, incubation which involves the creator's brain nonconscious searching for answers, lumination serves to discover the answer and find an answer and unity, and the creative production and verification.

Researchers have found the more mindful a person is when attempting a task (i.e., accepting their real-time emotions, connecting with themselves and the task at hand without judgment) the higher their cognitive, emotional, and interpersonal functioning is (Carson & Langer, 2006, Sedlmeier et al., 2012). The evidence suggests that practicing mindfulness intentionally helps boost these important, personal aspects. According to a meta-analysis by Lebuda, Zabelina, & Karwowski, mindfulness increases levels of healthy functioning in adults overall (Lebuda et al., 2015). Ultimately, creativity represents the ability to engage in divergent thinking and disengage from other accepted theories or practices and explore novelty through discovery.

Creativity Testing

Creativity is typically measured by the divergent thinking tests, during which participants are asked to name as many uses for a common object (e.g., brick) as possible within a limited amount of time (Guilford, 1967).

Responses are scored in terms of fluency (number of ideas), flexibility (number of categories), originality (the statistical novelty of responses), and elaboration (level of details). Other measures of creativity include self-report scales concerning creative behavior, personality, and activities (Baas et al., 2008; Simonton, 2012), or creative achievement (Carson et al., 2005). Less commonly utilized by creative researchers includes tasks with a single correct answer, such as insight-focused problems i.e., remote association tests (RAT; Mednick & Mednick, 1967).

Creative Mindfulness

We shall further explore how mindfulness and creativity have been conceptualized by others. Mindfulness is often associated with positive psychology and is considered a primary facet of psychological well-being (Langer, 2005; Kabat-Zinn, 2009; Brown & Ryan, 2003; Ivtzan et al., 2011). Mindful creativity is defined by Langer as "our creative nature is an integral part of our daily lives, expressed through our culture, our language, and even our most mundane activities" (Langer, 2005, p. 4). Langer examines aspects of creative mindfulness (Langer, 1989, 2005) which is an external stimulus positively associated with numerous aspects of well-being, including happiness, positive emotions, life satisfaction, vitality, sense of autonomy, optimism, self-regulation, and several aspects of cognitive performance (Brown et al., 2007; Keng et al., 2011; Langer, 2005).

Creativity and *Flow*

As we explore strength-based approaches to building resiliency, we will examine the qualities necessary to integrate creativity and mindfulness, which lead to the concept of *flow*. This shall offer us more tools available to empower a client towards intentional emotional healing. Csikszentmihalyi (1990) connected the creative moment with intentionality and when this event occurred, not by chance, "the best moments usually occur when a person's body or mind is stretched to its limits in a voluntary effort to accomplish something difficult and worthwhile" (p.3).

Maintaining a mindful approach and the act of conscious awareness leads to the ideal theoretical basis of *flow* as presented by Csikszentmihalyi (1996). This concept represents the intentionality of the individual to focus their psychic energy in the moment of the activity. The main feature of *flow* is an intense, experiential involvement in a moment-to-moment experience. It is the optimal state of attention and engagement, of the merger of action and awareness, with a loss of self-consciousness, an increase in self-control, a phenomenological experience of time, and an intrinsically rewarding experience (Nakamura & Csikszentmihalyi, 2002).

Flow is the state of total immersion, effortless concentration, and wrapt enjoyment in an activity in which one loses any sense of space, time, and self. *Flow* is defined as a state of operation, in which a person experiences full immersion in the activity he or she is doing. It often characterizes the experience of creativity and peak performance (Csikszentmihalyi et al., 2005). Much has been written about connecting mindfulness with creativity and creative approaches in connection with the Flow experience (Langer, 1989, 2005, 2014; Levy & Langer, 1994, 1999; Langer & Moldoveanu, 2000; Pirson et al., 2012).

This construct of *Flow* eventually led to the creation of Gendlin's Focusing art therapy (1998). Focusing is the act of listening to the body and the bodily responses and this felt sense approach makes use of the whole-body response while incorporating a creative approach towards understanding and empowerment (Friedman, 2005). Levy and Langer (1999) defined creativity as "the ability to transcend traditional ways of thinking by generating ideas, methods, and forms that are meaningful and new to others" (p. 45). They suggested that mindfulness facilitates creativity, while mindlessness impedes it. In her recent work on creativity, Langer (2014) argued that mindfulness and creativity are natural partners, because the key feature of mindfulness - the openness to new ideas - invokes the types of cognitive processes that are essential for creativity (e.g., curiosity, insight, analogical reasoning, remote associations, ideation). Dhiman (2012) suggested that the type of "mindful creativity" that Langer described is the gateway to the experience of flow (Csikszentmihalyi, 1990).

As noted earlier, the state of creative mindful awareness that Langer (2006) described is the cognitive groundwork from which the experience of *flow* can emerge (Csikszentmihalyi, 1990; Dhiman, 2012). Csikszentmihalyi (1992) explained that *flow* incorporates a unique mode of operation in which people are fully immersed in the activity they are doing, to the extent that the activity becomes semi-automated, and they become unaware of other events taking place around them, while, at the same time, they are alert and responsive of their creative insights. In other words, the paradox of flow is that it integrates the two states of mind—the automatic mode and the mindful one. Ultimately, mindfulness can serve as a basis of creativity, *flow*, and meaningful engagement of life and its myriad manifestations" (Dhiman, 2012).

Art Therapy

The experiences of creativity, mindfulness and *flow* lead us to the expressive process in mental health and counseling which is a field of study called *art therapy*. Since the middle of the twentieth century, mental health professionals called art therapists to work with clients and utilize "art media, the creative process, and the resulting artwork to explore their feelings, reconcile emotional conflicts, foster self-awareness, manage behavior and addictions, develop social skills, improve reality orientation, reduce anxiety, and increase self-esteem." (American Art Therapy Association, 2011). The use of these art therapy interventions served to promote mental, emotional, and physical healing according to Kaplan (2000) and Malchiodi (1999).

The emphasis of the art process as therapeutic was conceptualized by artist and art therapy pioneer, Edith Kramer (1916-2014). Ulman (2001) describes Kramer as concerned with "the healing quality inherent in the creative process" (p. 19). The other main voice in the psycho-dynamically oriented field was that of Margaret Naumburg (1890-1983) who explored art psychotherapy or the product as essential to the restorative process. Naumburg examined "the unconscious by means of spontaneous art expression" according to Ulman (2001, p.17).

Gladding (2011) identified the use of creativity and the arts for various therapeutic reasons including working through incongruence between what the individual thinks and the world around them. There is a tangible recording of the experience and allows for some distance from the content when an individual uses creativity to express their experiences. The piece of art created, is outside of the creator which provides distance, meaning, and insight to the artist.

Other therapeutic reasons include focusing on a goal allows for the participatory input/output of utilizing creative energy can be therapeutic and can lead to new ideas and enriching new experiences. Also, the act of personal expression is freeing to the content and to the emotion of the experience. Creativity and the arts encourage the building of resiliency and the creation of a new sense of self. The creative process allows the creator to conceptualize ideas to generate insight and increase greater self-esteem and self-rapport. The creative process can serve as a powerful and motivational experience for the creator. And, finally, the creative process, creativity, and the arts are by nature, are multicultural, and can be tailored specifically to the individualized creator (Gladding, 2011, p. 10).

Of consideration in our discussion is the natural reaction and response to new or different experiences that might be unique to the creator. As we have been reviewing, the creative process and creativity can be a deeply powerful experience that may lead to change behaviors. However, the utilization of creativity and the arts for insightful self-reflection can stimulate some defensive responses to the experience as well. The avoidance approach may be a natural response to situations in which individuals fear failure or a negative response. Elliot (2006) discussed humans experience avoidance as a motivation for successful adaptation of the experience; it facilitates survival that leads to aspects of thriving.

Now we know the approaches that are available, we shall integrate the research into a cogent, therapeutic process that strengthens emotional healing in traumatized individuals.

Narrative Process in Trauma Treatment

As we have previously reviewed, the client's personal experience is represented in their narrative of the trauma event. The exposure event is deeply personal and rooted in the brain and physiologically imprinted in the central nervous system. In fact, the individual and unique ways that trauma is processed impacts the retelling of the trauma story (Briere & Scott, 2006). The goal of treatment is to aid the traumatized client in the reintegration of their physiological response with their emotional experience. The process of inquiry represents the exploration of how an individual makes meaning of their inner, subjective realities.

Clandinin and Connelly (2000) discussed the process of alteration that may occur when individuals discuss their past, present, or future experiences. They acknowledged temporal changes that occurred when an individual shares their experiences and their lives. This process is not defined in linear terms but assumes that asking a question influences the nature of the answer. Narrative research maintains a concern for how the individual or group makes sense of the events or actions that have had some impact on their lives.

Ultimately, the use of narrative in the clinical mental health session allows the individual to tell their story from their own experiences. Mitchell and Egudo (2003) discussed narrative as effecting "cultural change, transfer complex tacit knowledge through implicit communication, construct identity, aid education, contribute to sense making, act as a source of understanding, and study decision making" (p. 3). In the utilization of narrative, the individual constructs their social story and shares it in their own unique manner of storytelling. This is where art, creativity, and culture allow for the personalization of the story for emotional healing. Diamond and Mullen (1999) discussed storytelling and the use of narrative in education to build creativity, complexity, and diversity in thinking.

References

Allen, N. B., Blashki, G., & Gullone, E. (2006). Mindfulness-based psychotherapies: A review of conceptual foundations, empirical evidence and practical considerations. *Australian and New Zealand Journal of Psychiatry, 40,* 285–294.

Amabile, T. M. (1996). *Creativity in context: Update to "The Social Psychology of Creativity."* Westview Press.

American Art Therapy Association. (2011). *American art therapy association.* Retrieved from http://www.americanarttherapyassociation.org/aata-aboutus.html

Baas, M., De Dreu, C. K. W., & Nijstad, B. A. (2008). A meta-analysis of 25 years of mood-creativity research: Hedonic tone, activation, or regulatory focus? *Psychological Bulletin, 134,* 779–806. http://dx.doi.org/ 10.1037/a0012815

Baer R. (2003). Mindfulness training as a clinical intervention: A conceptual and empirical review. *Clinical Psychology: Science and Practice, 10,* 125–143.

Bishop, S. R., Lau, M., Shapiro, S., Carlson, L., Anderson, N. D., & Carmody, J. F. (2004). Mindfulness: A proposed operational definition. *Clinical Psychology: Science & Practice, 11*, 230–241.

Bodhi, B. (1998). *The noble eightfold path: The way to the end of suffering.* Buddhist Publication Society. http://www.buddhanet.net/pdf_file/noble8path6.pdf

Bodhi, B. (2000). *The connected discourses of the Buddha* (p. 2080). Wisdom Publications

Briere, J., & Scott, C. (2006). *Principles of trauma therapy: A guide to symptoms, evaluation, and treatment.* Sage publications.

Bronowski J. (1972). *Science and human values.* New York: Harper and Rowe.

Brown, K. W., & Ryan, R. M. (2003). The benefits of being present: Mindfulness and its role in psychological well-being. *Journal of Personality and Social Psychology, 84*, 822–848.

Brown, K. W., Ryan, R. M., & Creswell, J. D. (2007). Addressing fundamental questions about mindfulness. *Psychological Inquiry, 18*(4), 272–281.

Carson, S. H., & Langer, E. J. (2006). Mindfulness and self-acceptance. *Journal of Rational-Emotive and Cognitive-Behavior Therapy, 24*(1), 29–43.

Carson, S., Peterson, J., & Higgins, D. (2005). Reliability, validity, and factor structure of the creative achievement questionnaire. *Creativity Research Journal, 17*, 37–50. DOI: 10.1207/s15326934crj1701_4

Cashwell, C. S., Bentley, D. P., & Bigbee, A. (2007). Spirituality and counselor wellness. *Journal of Humanistic Counseling, Education and Development, 46*, 66–81. DOI: 10.1002/j.2161-1939.2007.tb00026.x

Chiesa, A., Calati, R., & Serretti, A. (2011). Does mindfulness training improve cognitive abilities? A systematic review of neuropsychological findings. *Clinical Psychology Review, 31*(3), 449–464.

Chiesa, A., & Serretti, A. (2009). Mindfulness-based stress reduction for stress management in healthy people: A review and meta-analysis. *The Journal of Alternative and Complementary Medicine, 15*(5), 593–600.

Chiesa, A., & Serretti, A. (2010). A systematic review of neurobiological and clinical features of mindfulness meditations. *Psychological Medicine, 40*(8), 1239.

Clandinin, D. J., & Connelly F. M. (2000). *Narrative inquiry: Experience and story in qualitative research.* San Francisco: Jossey Bass, Inc.

Colzato, L. S., Ozturk, A., & Hommel, B. (2012). Meditate to create: The impact of focused-attention and open-monitoring training on convergent and divergent thinking. *Frontiers in Psychology, 3*, Art. no. 116. https://doi.org/10.33 89/fpsyg.2012.00116

Csikszentmihalyi, M. (1990). *Flow: The psychology of optimal experience.* Harper & Row. Retrieved from https://www.amazon.com/Flow-Psychology-Experience-Mihaly-Csikszentmihalyi/dp/0060162538?

Csikszentmihalyi, M. (1992). *Flow: The psychology of happiness.* Rider.

Csikszentmihalyi, M. (1996). *Creativity: Flow and the psychology of discovery and invention.* New York: Harper Perennial.

Csikszentmihalyi, M., Abuhamdeh, S., & Nakamura, J. (2005). *Flow.* In A. J. Elliot & C. S. Dweck (Eds.), *Handbook of competence and motivation* (pp. 598–608). Guilford Publications.

Davis, M. A. (2009). Understanding the relationship between mood and creativity: A meta-analysis. *Organizational Behavior and Human Decision Processes, 108*, 25–38. http://dx.doi.org/10.1016/j.obhdp.2008.04.001

De Dreu, C.K.W., Baas, M., & Nijstad, B.A. (2008). Hedonic tone and activation in themood–creativity link: Towards a dual pathway to creativity model. *Journal of Personality and Social Psychology, 94,* 739–756.

De Dreu, C., Nijstad, B., Baas, M., Wolsink, I., & Roskes, M. (2012). Working memory benefits creative insight, musical improvisation, and original ideation through maintained task-focused attention. *Personality & Social Psychology Bulletin, 38*(5), 656–669. https://doi.org/10.1177/0146167211435795

Dhiman, S. (2012). Mindfulness and the art of living creatively: Cultivating a creative life by minding our mind. *Journal of Social Change, 4*(1), 24–33.

Diamond, C. T., & Mullen, C. A. (1999). *The postmodern educator: Arts-based inquiries and teacher development.* New York: Peter Lang.

Ding, Y. Tang, Y. Deng, R. Tang, & M. I. Posner. (2015). Mood and personality predict improvement in creativity due to meditation training. *Learning and Individual Differences, 37,* 217–221.

Ding, X., Tang, Y. Y., & Tang, R. (2014). Improving creativity performance by short-term meditation. *Behavioral and Brain Functions, 10,* Art. no. 9. https://doi.org/10.1186/1744-9081-10-9

Elliot, A. (2006). The hierarchical model of approach-avoidance motivation. *Motivation and Emotion,* 30, 111–116. DOI: 10.1007/s11031-006-9028-7

Feldman, G., Hayes, A., Kumar, S., Greeson, J., & Laurenceau, J. P. (2007). Mindfulness and emotion regulation: The development and initial validation of the Cognitive and Affective Mindfulness Scale-Revised (CAMS-R). *Journal of Psychopathology and Behavioral Assessment, 29*(3), 177–190.

Friedman, N. (2005). Experiential listening. *Journal of Humanistic Psychology,* 45, 217–238.

Gendlin, E. T. (1998). *Focusing-oriented psychotherapy: A manual of the experiential method.* New York: Guilford Press.

Gladding, S. T. (2011). *The creative arts in counseling* (4th ed.). Alexandria, VA: American Counselling Association.

Greenberg, J., Reiner, K., & Meiran, N. (2012). Mind the trap: Mindfulness practice reduces cognitive rigidity. *PloS One, 7,* Art. no. e36206. DOI: 10.1371/journal.pone.0036206

Grossman, P., Niemann, L., Schmidt, S., & Walach, H. (2004). Mindfulness-based stress reduction and health benefits: A meta-analysis. *Journal of Psychosomatic Research, 57*(1), 35–43.

Guilford, J. P. (1967). Creativity: Yesterday, today, and tomorrow. *The Journal of Creative Behavior, 1*(1), 3–14. https://doi.org/10.1002/j.2162-6057.1967.tb00002.x

Hayes, S. C., & Smith, S. (2005). *Get out of your mind and into your life: The new acceptance and commitment therapy.* New Harbinger

Heilman K. M. (2016). Possible brain mechanisms of creativity. *Archives of Clinical Neuropsychology, 31*(4), 285–296.

Helmholtz, H. (1826). *Vortrage and reden. brunschweig: Vieweg* (p. 308). Cambridge: Cambridge University Press.

Ivtzan, I., Gardner, H. E., & Smailova, Z. (2011). Mindfulness meditation and curiosity: The contributing factors to wellbeing and the process of closing the self-discrepancy gap. *International Journal of Wellbeing, 1*(3), 316–326.

Jankowski, T., & Holas, P. (2014). Metacognitive model of mindfulness. *Consciousness and Cognition, 28,* 64–80. DOI: 10.1016/j.concog.2014.06.005. Epub 2014 Jul 18. PMID: 25038535.

Jedrczak, A., Beresford, M., & Clements, G. (1985). The TM-Sidhi program, pure consciousness, creativity, and intelligence. *The Journal of Creative Behavior,* 19, 270–275. https://doi.org/10.1002/j.2162-6057.1985.tb00409.x

Kabat-Zinn, J. (1990). *Full catastrophe living: Using the wisdom of your body and mind to face stress, pain, and illness.* New York, NY: Delacorte.

Kabat-Zinn, J. (1994). *Wherever you go there you are.* New York: Hyperion.

Kabat-Zinn, J. (2003). Mindfulness-based interventions in context: Past, present, and future. *Clinical Psychology: Science and Practice, 10*(2), 144–156.

Kabat-Zinn, J. (2009). *Letting everything become your teacher: 100 lessons in mindfulness.* Random House.

Kaplan, F. (2000). *Art, science and art therapy: Repainting the picture.* Jessica Kingsley Publishers.

Keng, S. L., Smoski, M. J., & Robins, C. J. (2011). Effects of mindfulness on psychological health: A review of empirical studies. *Clinical Psychology Review, 31*(6), 1041–1056.

Kostanski, M., & Hassed, C. (2008). Mindfulness as a concept and a process. *Australian Psychologist, 43*(1), 15–21.

Langer, E. J. (1989). *Mindfulness.* Addison-Wesley/Addison Wesley Longman.

Langer E. (2005). *On becoming an artist: Reinventing yourself through mindful creativity.* Ballantine Books.

Langer, E. J. (2014). *Mindfulness: 25th-anniversary edition.* Da Capo Press: Boston, MA.

Langer, E., & Moldoveanu, M. (2000). Mindfulness research and the future. *Journal of Social Issues, 56,* 129–139. DOI: 10.1111/0022-4537.00155

Lazar, S. W., Kerr, C. E., Wasserman, R. H., Gray, J. R., Greve, D. N., Treadway, M. T., & Fischl, B. (2005). Meditation experience is associated with increased cortical thickness. *Neuroreport, 16*(17), 1893–1897.

Lebuda, I., Zabelina, D., & Karwowski, M. (2015). Mind full of ideas: A meta-analysis of the mindfulness–creativity link. *Personality and Individual Differences, 93,* 1–5. DOI: 10.1016/j.paid.2015.09.040

Levy, B., & Langer, E. J. (1994). Aging free from negative stereotypes: Successful memory among the American Deaf and in Mainland China. *Journal of Personality and Social Psychology, 66,* 935–943.

Levy, B., & Langer, E. (1999). Aging. In M. A. Runco & S. R. Pritzker (Eds.), *Encyclopedia of creativity* (pp. 45–52). San Diego, CA: Elsevier

Lutz, A., Dunne, J., & Davidson, R. (2007). Meditation and the neuroscience of consciousness: An introduction. In P. Zelazo, M. Moscovitch, & E. Thompson (Eds.), *The Cambridge Handbook of consciousness* (Cambridge handbooks in psychology). Cambridge: Cambridge University Press. DOI: 10.1017/CBO9780511816789.020

Malchiodi, C. A. (1999). *Medical art therapy with adults.* London: Jessica Kingsley.

Mednick, S. A., & Mednick, M. T. (1967). *Examiner's manual: Remote Associates Test.* Boston, MA: Houghton Mifflin.

Meichenbaum, D. (1985). *Stress inoculation training.* New York: Pergamon.

Mitchell, M., & Egudo, M. (2003). *A review of narrative methodology* (pp. 1-39).

Edinburgh, Australia: Australian Government, Department of Defense, DSTO Systems Sciences Laboratory.

Moore, A., & Malinowski, P. (2009). Meditation, mindfulness and cognitive flexibility. *Consciousness and Cognition, 18*(1), 176–186.

Myer, J. E. & Sweeney, T. J. (2008). Wellness counseling: The evidence bases for practice. *Journal of Counseling and Development, 86*, 482–493.

Nakamura, J., & Csikszentmihalyi, M. (2002). The concept of flow. In C. R. Snyder & S. J. Lopez (Eds.), *Handbook of positive psychology* (pp. 89–105. New York: Oxford University Press.

Nijstad, B. A., De Dreu, C. K., Rietzschel, E. F., & Baas, M. (2010). The dual pathway to creativity model: Creative ideation as a function of flexibility and persistence. *European Review of Social Psychology, 21*(1), 34–77.

Pirson, M., Langer, E. J., Bodner, T., & Zilcha-Mano, S. (2012). The development and validation of the Langer mindfulness scale-enabling a socio-cognitive perspective of mindfulness in organizational contexts. *Fordham University Schools of Business Research Paper.*

Ostafin, B. D., & Kassman, K. T. (2012). Stepping out of history: Mindfulness improves insight problem-solving. *Consciousness and Cognition, 21*(2), 1031–1036.

Ren, J., Huang, Z. H., Luo, J., Wei, G. X., Ying, X. P., Ding, Z., Wu, Y., & Luo, F. (2011). Meditation promotes insightful problem-solving by keeping people in a mindful and alert conscious state. *Science China Life Sciences, 54*, 961–965.

Sedlmeier, P., Eberth, J., Schwarz, M., Zimmermann, D., Haarig, F., Jaeger, S., & Kunze, S. (2012, Nov.). The psychological effects of meditation: A meta-analysis. *Psychological Bulletin, 138*(6), 1139–1171. DOI: 10.1037/a0028168

Seligman, M. E. (2002). *Using the new positive psychology to realize your potential for lasting fulfillment: Authentic happiness.* New York: Free Press.

Shapiro, S. L. (2009). *The integration of mindfulness and psychology. Journal of Clinical Psychology, 65*(6), 555–560.

Shapiro, S. L., & Carlson, L. E. (2009). *The art and science of mindfulness: Integrating mindfulness into psychology and the helping professions.* Washington, D.C: American Psychological Association.

Shapiro, S. L., Carlson, L. E., Astin, J. A., & Freedman, B. (2006). Mechanisms of mindfulness. *Journal of Clinical Psychology, 62*, 373–386.

Siegel, D. (2007). *The mindful brain: Reflection and attunement in the cultivation of well-being.* New York: W.W. Norton & Company.

Simonton, D. (2012). Teaching creativity: Current findings, trends, and controversies in the psychology of creativity. *Teaching of Psychology, 39*(3), 217–222. https://doi.org/10.1177/0098628312450444

Simpson, L. R. (2005). *Level of spirituality as a predictor of the occurrence of compassion fatigue among counseling professionals in Mississippi.* The University of Mississippi.

Simpson, L. R., & Starkey, D. S. (2006). Secondary traumatic stress, compassion fatigue, and counselor spirituality: Implications for counselors working with trauma. Retrieved March 22, 2007, from http://www.counselingoutfitters.com/Simpsons.htm

Sternberg, R. J., & Lubart, T. I. (1996). Investing in creativity. *American Psychologist, 51*(7), 677–688. https://doi.org/10.1037/0003-066X.51.7.677

Thera, N. (1996). *The heart of Buddhist meditation*. York Beach, MN: Samuel Weiser.

Thompson, M., & Gauntlett-Gilbert, J. (2008). Mindfulness with children and adolescents: Effective clinical application. *Clinical Child Psychology and Psychiatry*, *13*(3), 395–407.

Ulman, E. (2001). Art therapy: Problems of definition. *American Journal of Art Therapy*, *40*(1), 16–26.

Wallas G. (1926). *The art of thought*. New York: Harcourt Brace.

Wallace, B. A. (2005). *Balancing the mind*. New York: Snow Lion.

Zabelina, M. D. Robinson, B. O. Ostafin, & J. C. Council. (2011). Manipulating mindfulness benefits creative elaboration at high levels of neuroticism. *Empirical Studies of the Arts*, *29*, 243–255

5 Resiliency and Wellness Approaches

The Resiliency Response

Trauma treatment focuses on building internalized feelings of strength and empowering the client for emotional betterment. Resiliency is the concept of growing and gaining strength after a traumatic experience has occurred (Bonanno & Mancini, 2008). As we have noted, altering the negative experience of trauma can have a profoundly positive impact on the individual, and building aspects of resilience may provide for effective neurobiological alteration to the brain.

The American Psychiatric Association (2013) has identified the growth response or *resilience* as "the process of adapting well in the face of adversity, trauma, tragedy, threats, or even significant sources of stress" (p. 2). The ability to *bounce back* from these adverse situations may offer protective factors that can enhance the biological processes of resiliency. These protective factors include susceptibility, prior experience to managing stress levels, and early life experiences that produce long-lasting hormonal, neurotransmitters, and central nervous system changes (Luthar & Cicchetti, 2000).

Various resiliency constructs have focused on the neuronal adaption and strength-based approach to trauma. For example, Wagnild (2010) describes the *resilience core* as the resilient characteristics that support an individual's awareness of self, perseverance, balance and harmonious viewpoint in life, problem-solving abilities, and comfort within oneself. As we continue discussing methods of building resilience, we shall be aware of the related concept of wellness and its usage in clinical mental health work. Resilience is further strengthened by multiple potential psychosocial factors (Feder et al., 2010). These protective factors include active coping strategies of planning and problem-solving. Facing one's fears is a proactive stance that is difficult for individuals dealing with PTSD symptoms, as many will avoid triggers subsequently continuing the fear response (Feder et al., 2010).

Another protective factor for psychological resiliency includes a strength-based disposition to buffer against the adverse results of the stress response.

DOI: 10.4324/9781003030591-5

It decreases the autonomic arousal produced by negative emotions and reduces the stress reactivity (Feder et al., 2010). The active construction of a cognitive appraisal system is a reframing behavior that allows for multiple avenues of thought and an increase in well-being (Seligman, 2006).

Social support is an important protective factor for individuals dealing with stress and stress-related issues (Skobal, 2010). Secure attachments aid in reducing the negative effects of physical injury and emotional distress. Feder et al. (2010) discuss how creating a purpose aids in trauma recovery. Finally, maintaining a purposeful life assists in creating an additional level of protection. Let us examine the impact that the process of resiliency has on cellular levels of learning of the human brain.

Learning at the Cellular Level

Cellular learning occurs most effectively with converging multisensory input. For example, when we learn using one sensory modality it takes more time and effort to master that task and form a memory, however learning with using two modalities, the converging sensory information will expedite our learning (Grabner et al., 2006). Muscle memory is the brain's requiring significant resources to make unfamiliar behaviors routine, but as the brain adapts, efficient networks develop that require less effort for learning. The experience of the practice increases the muscle memory and thus requires less effort over time. The repetition of the action causes neuronal evolution throughout the brain and builds muscle memory.

The process of forming healthy self-reflective habits leads to an examination of habit development. Past theories on the process of habit formation include Abraham Myerson's (1921) work which discussed how the living tissue of the brain's memory is crossed by a stimulus. He considered how the memory system becomes more permeable, easier to activate, and with consciousness and can lead to habit. Over time, this process integrates into automatic behavior. Seminal theories by Watson (1913), and Skinner's influential *behaviorism theory* (1938) directly connect this formation of habit to behavior. This theory grew out of the earlier work of Thorndike (1898) and his notion of learning which identified a bond between a physical or sensory event and the muscle reflexivity causing the response.

Learning involves the creation of new and technical expertise through the repetition of a particular behavior. Skill learning is a training approach that demands full conscious attention until the skill becomes that of automatic, subconscious behavior. The skill learning remains in working memory until it is shifted into long-term memory storage. Other parts of the brain assist to provide value-meaning associations, motor abilities, verbal directions, hearing, intermediate memory, and spatial imagination (Tan, 2007). Other learning approaches may involve the use of reflection.

Individuals can facilitate learning between the cognitive experience and conceptual aspects of consciousness. Reflection is a tool that allows for the integration of "cognitive and non-conceptual elements that make up our experience and consciousness" (Jordi, 2011, p. 182). Contemplation is an approach that combines the use of rational learning with sensory experiences. The focus is on the shift from pondering to a capacity of deeper awareness and insight. Other cultures have found contemplation as an effective approach for traditions of wisdom, where Western cultures have focused on the natural sciences and the scientific approaches. Buddhism, Hindu, Jewish Kabbalah, and Asian traditions have embraced contemplative approaches for thousands of years (Hart, 2004).

Wellness

The clinical mental health field recognizes the importance of wellness with mental health counselors. The most recent codes surrounding counselor wellness are stated by the professional and governing boards in the counseling field. The American Counseling Association Code of Ethics requires that "counselors engage in self-care activities to maintain and promote their emotional, physical, mental, and spiritual well-being to meet their professional responsibilities" (American Counseling Association, 2014, p. 8). Other credentialing boards focus on the need for self-care strategies in very general terms. Council for Accreditation of Counseling and Related Educational Programs (2009) encourages "self-care strategies appropriate to the counselor role" (Section II, G.1.d).

The World Health Organization [WHO], 2020 defined mental health as the state of wellbeing in which an individual realizes their capabilities to combat normal life stressors and work competencies in contributing to the belonged community, which is underpinned by six psychological elements comprising (i) self-acceptance, (ii) meaning in life, (iii) autonomy, (iv) healthy relationships with others, (v) environmental mastery, and (vi) personal growth (Mukhtar 2020).

According to Larson (1999), wellness is described as a new paradigm in the healthcare field which incorporates a strength-based approach to mental health care (Smith, 2001). An *Indivisible Self* is an evidence-based model of wellness based on the earlier wellness model, the Wheel of Wellness. Both models originate out of the theory incorporated within Adler's Individual Psychology movement (Sweeney, 1998). The idea of holism and purposeful were the key points towards understanding human behavior. This wellness model incorporated five different factors of the "coping self," "creative self," "physical self," "essential self," and "social self" (Myers & Sweeney, 2004). Myers and Sweeney (2008) discussed the wellness paradigm which provides strength-based strategies to conceptualize issues and plan interventions for optimal growth. The CMT approach provides the individual with the necessity for wellness and building strength-based approaches for self-care.

Resiliency Research

Resilience is conceptualized within this manuscript as the process, or the achievement, of positive coping strategies despite difficult or challenging situations. It consists of a set of personality traits that offer protection from the negative effects of stress which include the ability to handle, change, or maintain the personal resources to control the effects of the stressors as needed. Resiliency involves the process of being exposed to traumatic material and emotionally growing from the experience.

Critical abilities of resilient individuals included: mastery of resources (Gil & Weinberg, 2015), capacity for positive emotions (Kok & Fredrickson, 2013), an internal locus of control (Agaibi & Wilson, 2005), and availability of social support and interpersonal security (Meredith et al., 2008). Personality traits were found to contribute to the cognitive and emotional flexibility needed to disclose, explain, and process trauma in therapy and return to baseline levels of life satisfaction (Park et al., 2004). Optimism, flexibility, insight, self-confidence, aptitude for meaning-making, self-care, and identification as a survivor rather than a victim, were some examples (Maddi, 2006). Other characteristics that contributed to resiliency include the capacity for creativity (Gallagher & Lopez, 2007), imagination (Kalmanowitz & Ho, 2016), and the appreciation of beauty (Peterson et al., 2006). Strength-based treatment approaches that have also been suggested as contributors to resiliency include short-term group psychotherapy and single sessions, which are based on findings that most therapeutic changes occurred in the first couple of sessions (Başoglu et al., 2007; Slive & Bobele, 2012).

Creative Well-Being

Despite the negative and harmful effects of the stress response on the system, it is important to note the positivistic or strength-based response from exposure to traumatic material. Resiliency is an aspect of the counseling experience that provides moments of internal emotional development within the client. The practice of being creative can serve to enhance learning as well as increase mental capacities and promote wellness thus building the construct of resilience. Gladding (2011) creativity and the arts have been known to assist individuals in creating their personal moments of insight and learning. Harter (2007) offers the possibility that visual art-making may "better capture tacit emotional nuances and an emerging edge of experience" (p. 167).
Harter 2007

Mindful Research

Mindfulness-based research has been exploring approaches to incorporate the various approaches of mindful, trauma-focused, and creative approaches in clinical-based experiences. For example, *mindfulness-based relapse prevention* (MBRP), *mindfulness-based art therapy* (MBAT), and *mindfulness-based relationship enhancement* (MBRE; Shapiro & Carlson, 2009).

Creative Wellness

Research on the topic of creativity found that "creative activity can have an impact on mental well-being" (Leckey, 2011, p. 501). The use of creativity serves multiple purposes and goals. Rollo May (1975) explored the act of being creative as "courageous" and that creativity is "bringing something new into being" (p. 37). Creativity requires courage to create and confront deeply personal material and the integrity to explicitly consider and revise (Kelly, 1991).

The process of utilizing creativity brings about increased opportunities for wellness and balance. Many authors have incorporated the creative process into the realm of wellness or more specific approaches to supporting individuals with trauma. Short (2017) explores the utilization of art and mindful journaling into the eight stages of wellness that include examining and incorporating social, environmental, physical, emotional, spiritual, occupational, intellectual, and financial considerations into life for the balance and emotional harmony for living.

Other Creative Protocols

Other researchers have explored variations of these approaches and established alternative Creative Protocols. *Trauma and the Expressive Arts* from Malchiodi (2020) describe ways to tap into deeply felt bodily and sensory experiences as a foundation for safely exploring emotions, memories, and personal narratives. The *Expressive Therapies Continuum*, a neuroscience approach that was used to treat trauma and highlights levels of processing (Hinz, 2019). Another approach is the *Focus-Oriented Arts Therapy (FOAT)* by Laury Rapport (2008) which accesses the body's wisdom and creative intelligence through the act of focusing on various mindfulness-based approaches and art therapies (Rappaport, 2008, 2014). The principles of FOAT utilize presence, grounding, focusing attitude, listening, and reflection, and clinical sensitivity while working with clients. FOAT involves being able to ask the accepting question of "are you there in present in your own body, mind, and spirit?" Grounding includes the centering of the body through breath and body awareness. Focusing attitude involves the loving attitude towards oneself and welcoming one's inner felt sense. Bessel Van der Kolk discusses how paying attention to the body's physical sensations, "we can recognize the ebb and flow of our emotions, and with that, increase our control over them" (2014, p. 208). Listening and reflection "demonstrate compassionate understanding through experiential listening, artistic reflection, and non-verbal communication (i.e., gesture, energy, movement)" (Rappaport, 2014, p. 195). Clinical sensitivity involves being mindful of each client's needs in the moment.

Instinctual Trauma Response (ITR) is a neuroscientific model with an art therapy protocol that was developed for diverse types of severe trauma. It emphasized drawing a graphic narrative and having the therapist re-present the story back to the survivor (Gantt & Tinnin, 2009). More specific to *Combat-Related PTSD*, Spiegel et al. (2006) recommended a three-stage art therapy model, which involved: (a) reducing arousal and increasing social bonding, (b) processing memories, and (c) attaining insight. For the same population, Naff (2014), suggested: (a) containment and security, (b) narration and exposure allowance, (c) integration, and (d) maintenance.

Meekums (1999) proposed an *Internal-Trauma Processing Model* that consists of (a) striving, (b) incubation, (c) new perspective, and (d) re-evaluation, whereas Rankin & Taucher (2003) considered a six-task oriented approach: safety planning, self-management, telling the trauma story, grieving losses, self-concept and worldview revision, and self-relational-development.

Another research approach was the *four-drawing art therapy trauma and resiliency protocol study* which found the trauma types to include relational versus non-relational trauma, and single incident versus chronic-complex trauma. The impact of trauma was shown to depend on the perceived degree of threat to self and others, resiliency, and environmental factors (Agaibi & Wilson, 2005), including relational insecurity and loneliness (Meredith et al., 2008), negative self-views (Sutherland & Bryant, 2005), and chronic pain (Liedl et al., 2010).

Mental and Physical Health Outcomes

Current traumatology-focused research has been focusing on the concept of resilience and investigating the mechanisms that prevent illness and support strength-based approaches towards treatment (Kalisch et al., 2014). There is a paradigm shift in mental health research and counseling, centering on the development of novel prevention and treatment strategies that focus more on resilience and less on psychopathology. The goal of this approach is to counter the neurobiological response of trauma and enhance current strength-based approaches that build resilience within the client (McCleary & Figley, 2017; Osório et al., 2017). The importance of building resiliency supports the clinical mental health process as well as adding approaches to adapting and altering the stress response, ensuring the counselor will recognize the physiological experience of the trauma and safeguard efficacious techniques.

Reference for Chapter 5

American Psychiatric Association. (2013). *Diagnostic and statistical manual of mental disorders* (5th ed.). Arlington, VA: American Psychiatric Association.

American Counseling Association. (2014). *ACA code of ethics*. Alexandria, VA: American Psychiatric Association.

Agaibi, C. E., & Wilson, J. P. (2005, Jul.). Trauma, PTSD, and resilience: A review of the literature. *Trauma Violence Abuse*, 6(3), 195–216. DOI: 10.11 77/1524838005277438. PMID: 16237155.

Başoglu, M., Salcioglu, E., & Livanou, M. (2007, Feb.). A randomized controlled study of single-session behavioral treatment of earthquake-related post-traumatic stress disorder using an earthquake simulator. *Psychological Medicine*, 37(2), 203–213. DOI: 10.1017/S0033291706009123. PMID: 17254365.

Bonanno, G. A., & Mancini, A. D. (2008). The human capacity to thrive in the face of potential trauma. *Pediatrics*, 121, 369–375.

Council for Accreditation of Counseling and Related Educational Programs. (2009). *2009 Standards*. Retrieved from http://www.cacrep.org/doc/2009%2 0Standards.pdf

Duch, W. (2007). A.-G. Tan (Ed.). *Creativity and the brain: A handbook of creativity for teachers* (pp. 507–530). Singapore: World Scientific Publishing.

Duerr, M., Zajonc, A., & Dana, D. (2003). Survey of transformative and spiritual dimensions of higher education. *Journal of Transformative Education, 1*(3), 177–211.

Feder, A., Nestle, E. J., Westphal, M., & Charney, D.S. (2010). Psychobiological mechanisms of resilience to stress. In J. W. Reich, A. J. Zautra, & J. S. Hall (Eds.), *Handbook of adult resilience* (pp. 35–54). New York: Guilford Press

Gallagher, M. W., & Lopez, S. J. (2007). Curiosity and well-being. *The Journal of Positive Psychology*, 2(4), 236–248. https://doi.org/10.1080/17439760701552345

Gantt, L., & Tinnin, L. W. (2009). Support for a neurobiological view of trauma with implications for art therapy. *The Arts in Psychotherapy*, 36(3), 148–153. https://doi.org/10.1016/j.aip.2008.12.005

Gil, S., & Weinberg, M. (2015). Coping strategies and internal resources of dispositional optimism and mastery as predictors of traumatic exposure and of PTSD symptoms: A prospective study. *Psychological Trauma: Theory, Research, Practice, and Policy*, 7(4), 405–411. https://doi.org/10.1037/tra0000032

Gladding, S.T. (2011). *The creative arts in counseling*. Alexandria, VA: The American Counseling Association.

Grabner, R. H., Neubauer A. C., & Stern E. (2006, Apr.). Superior performance and neural efficiency: the impact of intelligence and expertise. *Brain Research Bulletin, 69*(4), 422–439. DOI: 10.1016/j.brainresbull.2006.02.009. Epub 2006 Mar 3. PMID: 16624674.

Hart, T. (2004). Opening the contemplative mind in the classroom. *Journal of Transformative Education, 2*(1), 28–46.

Harter, S. L. (2007). Visual art-making for therapist growth and self-care. *Journal of Constructivist Psychology*, 20(2), 167–182.

Hinz, L. D. (2019). *Expressive therapies continuum: A framework for using art in therapy* (2nd ed.). Routledge. https://doi.org/10.4324/9780429299339

Jordi, R. (2011). Reframing the concept of reflection: Consciousness, experiential learning, and reflective learning practices. *Adult Education Quarterly, 61*(2), 181–197.

Kalisch, R., Müller, M. B., & Tüscher, O. (2014). A conceptual framework for the neurobiological study of resilience. *Behavioral and Brain Sciences, 38*, Art. no. e92. DOI: 10.1017/S0140525X1400082X

Kalmanowitz, D., & Ho, R. T. H. (2016). Out of our mind. Art therapy and mindfulness with refugees, political violence, and trauma. *The Arts in Psychotherapy, 49*, 57–65. https://doi.org/10.1016/j.aip.2016.05.012

Kelly, G.A. (1991). *The psychology of personal constructs* (vols. 1 and 2). New York: Routledge.

Kok, B. E., & Fredrickson, B. L. (2013). Positive emotion: How positive emotions broaden and build. In J. J. Froh & A. C. Parks (Eds.), *Activities for teaching positive psychology: A guide for instructors* (pp. 61–63). American Psychological Association. https://doi.org/10.1037/14042-010

Leykin, D., Lahad, M., Cohen, O., Goldberg, A., & Aharonson-Daniel, L. (2013). Conjoint community resiliency assessment measure-28/10 Items (CCRAM28 and CCRAM10): A self-report tool for assessing community resilience. *American Journal of Community Psychology, 52*, 313–323. DOI: 10.1 007/s10464-013-9596-0

Larson, J. S. (1999). The conceptualization of health. *Medical Care Research and Review, 56*, 123–136.

Leckey, J. (2011). The therapeutic effectiveness of creative activities on mental well-being: a systematic review of the literature. *Journal of Psychiatric Mental Health Nursing, 18*, 501–509.

Liedl, A., O'Donnell, M., Creamer, M., Silove, D., McFarlane, A., Knaevelsrud, C., & Bryant, R. A. (2010, Jul.). Support for the mutual maintenance of pain and post-traumatic stress disorder symptoms. *Psychological Medicine, 40*(7), 1215–1223. DOI: 10.1017/S0033291709991310. Epub 2009 Oct 8. PMID: 19811699.

Luthar, S. S., & Cicchetti, D. (2000). The construct of resilience: Implications for interventions and social policies. *NIHPA Author Manuscripts, 12*(4), 1–32.

Maddi, S. (2006). Hardiness: The courage to grow from stress. *The Journal of Positive Psychology, 1*, 160–168. DOI: 10.1080/17439760600619609

Malchiodi, C. A. (2020). *Trauma and expressive arts therapy: Brain, body, and imagination in the healing process.* New York: Guilford Press.

May, R. (1975). *The courage to create.* New York: Bantam Books.

McCleary, J., & Figley, C. (2017). Resilience and trauma: Expanding definitions, uses, and contexts [Editorial]. *Traumatology, 23*(1), 1–3. https://doi.org/10.103 7/trm0000103

Meekums, B. (1999). A creative model for recovery from child sexual abuse trauma. *The Arts in Psychotherapy, 26*(4), 247–259.

Meredith, P., Ownsworth, T., & Strong, J. (2008). A review of the evidence linking adult attachment theory and chronic pain: Presenting a conceptual model. *Clinical Psychology Review, 28*(3), 407–429. DOI: 10.1016/j.cpr.2007.07.009

Mukhtar, S. (2020). Pakistanis' mental health during the COVID-19. *Asian Journal of Psychiatry, 51*, Art. no. 102127. https://doi.org/10.1016/j.ajp.2020.1 02127

Myers, J. E., & Sweeney, T. J. (2004). The indivisible self: An evidence-based model of wellness. *Journal of Individual Psychology, 60*(3), 234–245.

Myer, J. E. & Sweeney, T. J. (2008). Wellness counseling: The evidence bases for practice. *Journal of Counseling and Development, 86*, 482–493.

Myerson, A. (1921). *The foundations of personality*. New York: Little, Brown, and Co.

Naff, K. (2014). A framework for treating cumulative trauma with art therapy. *Art Therapy, 31*(2), 79–86.

Osório, C., Probert, T., Jones, E., Young, A. H., & Robbins, I. (2017, Oct.–Dec.). Adapting to stress: Understanding the neurobiology of resilience. *Behavioral Medicine, 43*(4), 307–322. DOI: 10.1080/08964289.2016.1170661. Epub 2016 Apr 21. PMID: 27100966.

Park, N., Peterson, C., & Seligman, M. (2004). Strengths of character and well-being. *Journal of Social and Clinical Psychology, 23*(5), 603–619.

Peterson, C., Park, N., & Seligman, M. E. (2006). Greater strengths of character and recovery from illness. *The Journal of Positive Psychology, 1*(1), 17–26.

Rankin, A. B., & Taucher, L. C. (2003) A task-oriented approach to art therapy in trauma treatment, *Art Therapy, 20*(3), 138–147. DOI:10.1080/07421656.2003.10129570

Rappaport, L. (2008). Focusing-oriented art therapy. *The Folio: A Journal for Focusing and Experiential Therapy, 21*(1), 139–155.

Rappaport, L. (Ed.). (2014). *Mindfulness and the arts therapies: Theory and practice*. London: Jessica Kingsley Publishers.

Seligman, M. (2006). *Learned optimism: How to change your mind and your life*. New York City: Random House.

Shapiro, S. L., & Carlson, L. E. (2009). *The art and science of mindfulness: Integrating mindfulness into psychology and the helping professions*. Washington, D.C: American Psychological Association.

Short, B. A. (2017). *Creative wellness: Art journaling with mindfulness*. Oregon: Beth Short.

Skinner, B. F. (1938). *The behavior of organisms*. New York: Appleton-Century-Crofts.

Skobal, A.E. (2010). The resilient personality. In J. W. Reich, A. J. Zautra, & J. S. Hall (Eds.), *Handbook of adult resilience* (pp. 112–125). New York: Guilford Press.

Slive, A., & Bobele, M. (2012). Walk-in counseling services: Making the most of one hour. *Australian and New Zealand Journal of Family Therapy, 33*(1), 27–38.

Smith, H. (2001). Professional identity for counselors. In D. C. Locke, J. E. Myers, & E. H. Herr (Eds.), *The handbook of counseling*. Thousand Oaks, CA: Sage Publications.

Spiegel, D., Malchiodi, C., Backos, A., & Collie, K. (2006). Art therapy for combat-related PTSD: Recommendations for research and practice. *Art Therapy, 23*(4), 157–164.

Sutherland, K., & Bryant, R. A. (2005). Self-defining memories in post-traumatic stress disorder. *British Journal of Clinical Psychology, 44*(4), 591–598. https://doi.org/10.1348/014466505x64081

Sweeney, T. J. (1998). *Adlerian counseling: A practitioner's approach* (4th ed.). Philadelphia: Taylor & Francis.

Thorndike, E. L. (1898). Animal intelligence: An experimental study of the associative processes in animals. *Psychological Review Monograph Supplement, 2*, 1–109.

Van der Kolk, B. (2014). *The body keeps the score: Brain, mind, and body in the healing of trauma*. New York: Penguin Group.

Wagnild, G. M. (2010). Discovering your resilience core. Available at: http://www.resiliencescale.com/papers/pdfs/Discovering_Your_Resilience_Core.pdf

Watson, J. B. (1913). Psychology as the behaviorist views it. *Psychological Review, 20,* 158–177.

World Health Organization (WHO). (2009). Disease and injury regional estimates for 2004. Geneva, Switzerland. Survey Replication. *Archives of General Psychiatry, 62*(6), 593–602. https://covid19.who.int/

6 Examples of Creative Mindfulness Techniques

Creative Mindfulness Techniques

We shall synthesize all that we have learned in this exploration of the creative mindfulness approach. We can recognize that as human beings and visual thinkers, we have a proclivity to organize thoughts, feelings, and perceptions about lived experiences in images and imagery. By allowing problems, emotions, or concerns to be represented in a visual manner, there is understanding through the expressive process. This lucidity and physical separation from the creation allows for a deeper, more reflective experience of the struggle.

The creator of the work is the expert of their creative expression and only they can provide a truly accurate analysis of the work. However, restatements of the visual facts or emotional experiences of the observer may be indicative of internalized struggles for the creator. For example, omissions, erasures, and alterations are all suggestions of symbolic communication from the internal experiences of the creator (Ulman, 2001). The emotional reparation and personal transformation come from the creator's interaction and reflection with the created piece, with the material presented within the active dialogue, and with the connection to the clinician.

Ethical Disclaimer

My cautionary ethical disclaimer is one that is spoken of in all art therapy training programs. Determine your client intervention based on the anticipated goals and choose the materials with knowledge and insight into the possible outcomes of the responsiveness. Responsiveness by the client to the material, the responsiveness of the material to the artist, and responsiveness of the clinician to the overall experience. Preparation is key to supporting the experience of creation in counseling in a professional and ethically sound manner. Consider what your treatment goals represent and how you will support your client throughout the entire process and above all else, the ethical consideration to "do no harm" should always be relevant and forefront of the discussion.

DOI: 10.4324/9781003030591-6

Media Expectations of the Various Properties

Art materials maintain different qualities and should be chosen to enhance the narrative experiences of the individual. There is a connection between the kinesthetic-motor and sensory-tactile areas of the brain which aid in facilitating imagery formation through "sensory stimulation, exploration and play with art media (Lusebrink, 2004, p. 129). Art media is described as having qualities on a continuum description scale. For example, paper is scaled from porous to smooth in texture. Paint such as acrylic paint is fluid due to the addition of water and the liquid nature, thus making it difficult to control. On the continuum scale, we compare paint to wax-based crayons, which are easier to control and require no other elements such as water or brushes. Clay may be considered controlled when using fast drying, air dry clay unless compared to earthen clay which is a natural, finely grained soil material that must be manipulated and fired.

Control in Material Choice

Art media exists on a continuum from most structured to least structured. When utilizing art for a therapeutic situation, it is important to select the most appropriate medium; it is dependent on the desired effect and the needs of the client. Materials the provide the most structure or control is the cellular camera, graphite pencils, and colored pencils. They are easy to control, precise, and allow for editing, erasing, and starting over. Also, easy to work with and supportive include images for collage, stamps, and pens or markers.

Less structured or more fluid materials are at the other end of the continuum and include watercolor paints, oil paint, and clay which are more difficult to control. The choice of art materials for utilization with a client is akin to the consideration for the appropriate intervention with a client. The type of material, quality of the material, and the basic responsiveness of the material become important. The expectation for the material and material choice should be found within the needs of the client. How much control do they require? Is the individual able to withstand a limited amount of control and is this a treatment goal? Let us explore some examples of easily accessible materials for therapeutic effectiveness.

Easily Accessible Materials with Prompts

Written Letters to Remind a Client about Self-Care

Figure 6.1 represents an example of the use of written letters placed in an envelope that the client has written self-care approach words. In this case, the letter was written by the client and then mailed back to the client to

Figure 6.1 Self-care letter.

remind them of the work that is required. **Prompts:** Write out a list of items that you require for your personal self-care? Which of these items are you currently doing? What do you need to complete your list of self-care approaches daily? Weekly? Who is in control of this process? **Long-term Prompt:** Write out the list for self-care and mail it back to the client in a few weeks or months for a reminder.

Tell Stories/Narratives to Discuss Individual Strength

Figure 6.2 represents a digital photograph of a turtle keeping its head about the foam of the incoming tide of water. This metaphor represents how a client might find that identifies their approach to difficulty. In this case, the client felt in control and their head was above water, in some cases, the client might feel that they are getting swept away by the incoming tide. **Prompts:** What is happening in this image and where is the strength coming from? What kind of support is needed to be successful in this image? How do you relate to this process? Do you see a victim or a survivor/thriver? How is safety created?

Cellular Photograph of Calming Places the Client likes to Visit

Figure 6.3 represents a digital image of a place that represents calm or relaxed feelings such as the grassy beach before walking near the calm

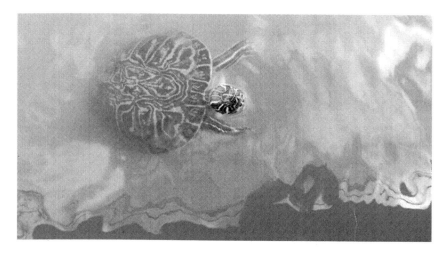

Figure 6.2 Turtle.

Figure 6.3 Windy wheat.

ocean on a summer day. The narrative about this location is important to understand. The client identified calm and relaxation, but for other client's there might be some darkness or an impending storm on the horizon. **Prompt:** Tell a story/narrative about this image. Where is this calming place located? What makes it a calming space? How would you add aspects of this location to your personal world?

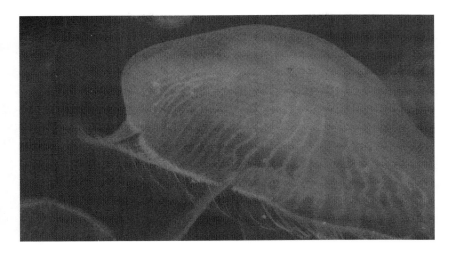

Figure 6.4 Jellyfish.

Images for Guidance in Writing, Poetry, or Lyrics for Songs

Figure 6.4 represents a client's focus on creativity and storytelling about a nebulous image of an invertebrate animal. In this case, a jellyfish image was chosen to allow openness for creativity. **Prompt:** Write a song/poetry about this image of a jellyfish. How does a jellyfish flow in the ocean? Connect it to the flow of the song or poem.

Pattern Drawings Can be Calming

Figure 6.5 represents a client's decision to utilize controlled materials that felt comfortable such as a pen and ink pattern drawing on white paper. The client felt the control of the material and of the subject matter without many decisions having to be made including black and white without color. **Prompts:** Start with pen and paper and make a mark on the page and add more lines. How does it feel? What is the artist thinking? **Prompt Variation**: Add calming music to the working session. What is the emotion word as the client starts the process? What is the emotional word as the client completes the process?

Explore Concepts from a Distance

Figure 6.6 represents a water scene that allows the client a chance to explore concepts from a distance such as at the water edge overlooking a dock on a sunny day. The distance might allow a client to explore an idea without getting too close such as they had a fear or phobia. **Prompts:** Where would

Figure 6.5 Pen and ink line drawing.

Figure 6.6 Water Scene that represents calmness and stillness.

you like to be? Where are you afraid to be? Tell a story about the fear and about the strength within. **Prompt Variations:** Add aspects of mindfulness and breathing to this experience? What do you notice within your body as you think and feel this moment? Add Mindful Meditation Script (**See Appendix B).**

Creative Mindfulness Techniques

The original Creative Mindfulness Technique (CMT) was written by Costello (2015) and focused on the integration of the Creative Mindfulness training into a 6-week counselor education training that provided an opportunity for building resiliency levels and wellness aspects through deeper, more internalized, and self-reflective counselor learning. The mindfulness model infused with aspects of creativity enhanced the strong base of the new counselor, decreased levels of counselor anxiety, and provided opportunities for long-term effectiveness and longevity within the counseling field (**See Appendix A).**

The goal was to seek a more transformational and transpersonal method of counselor development for wellness that will assist the counselor, the counseling field, and the future counseling clients. The process included mindful training, breathwork, and active dialogue about various strength-based information on Trauma/Vicarious Trauma/Coping/Wellness/Resiliency. The participants were asked to make an artistic expression about coping, wellness, resiliency. The creative process allows the creator to conceptualize ideas to generate insight and increase greater self-esteem and self-rapport. Finally, the creative process, creativity, and the arts are by nature, multicultural and tailored specifically to the individualized creator (Gladding, 2011, p. 10).

The results identified that the process of CMT could assist in building concepts of wellness and self-care, as well as be easily incorporated into counselor education programs thus making it a viable approach. It is necessary to allow students time and support while building self-care levels, whether it is through incorporating some CMT techniques into counseling courses or adding them as an element of supervision. The approach can easily be adapted to most classroom situations and provides another method towards self-reflective learning and deeper levels of understanding of wellness and self-care.

The experience of creativity can enhance the process of building resiliency. "Resilience can be manifest in and nurtured by creativity" according to Parr et al. (1998, p. 27). Creativity can allow for problem-solving approaches to elucidate new and alternative solutions. Creativity encourages an active and resilient approach towards enhancing the creator's viewpoint for new learning considerations. The following case examples represent various approaches to effective integration of the CMT process with various clinical processes a mental health clinician might experience. Note the flexibility that is necessary for offering the experience to clinicians, students, and clients alike. Remember the intention is for supportive and strength-based learning opportunities that lead to moments of resiliency. Our first case focused on the use of Creative Mindfulness Techniques in supporting a counselor in their professional development through supervision.

Case Figure 1 CMT for Supervision Purposes

CMT Directive

The CMT directive was provided to a counseling supervisee who was asked to *create an artistic expression on your outlook on life since becoming a counselor.* The directive was presented for the purposes of supervision through the self-reflective lens and was based on important developmental concepts presented in their counselor training program. In Case Figure 6.7, the artwork was made with the use of acrylic paints on mixed media paper.

Reflections After the Creative Work

"When I think of my outlook on life as an emerging counselor, I think of all of the new growth that I've experienced lately. Some areas have been challenging to work through because they have required me to dig deep and face some truths that I have been unwilling or unable to explore previously. This is represented by the dark wisps around the edges of the image. However, this outlook is a largely positive one. It feels warm and bright and colorful and inviting, much like the multicolored sun shining out from behind the plant and radiating throughout the image. The plant is shrouded by light yellow rays of hope, which extend through the piece, keeping the darkness at bay and even shattering it all together in some places."

Case Figure 2 CMT and Self-Awareness for Cultural Considerations

CMT Directive

The CMT approach with the supervision focus, for this counseling student, represented their exploration of national issues impacting the current media and recent cultural protest movements. The artist was asked to *Create an Artistic Expression* and titled the piece *In Times of #BlackLivesMatter.* Colored pencils, chalk pastels, and washable markers were utilized across two pieces of heavy-weight, multimedia paper (5.5 × 5.5"). Figure 6.8 was created to represent the current cultural concerns and protest movements that the student was witnessing in her daily life.

Figure 6.7 CMT for Supervision Purposes.
Permission by Artist.

Figure 6.8 CMT and Self-Awareness for Cultural Considerations.
Permission by Artist.

Reflections After the Creative Work

"Following the outcome of Breonna Taylor's case, I reflected on the Black Lives Matter movement. I allowed myself to feel guilt for the ways in which I have unknowingly perpetuated systems of oppression and for the fact that I will never truly know the lived experience of black folks in this country. What I also realized is that I do know the constant fear of losing the people I love most. I also know the pain of watching them hurt and of watching a community suffer. So, I responded to two prompts: 1: how does it feel to love a black man, when black lives do not. matter. 2: how does it feel to love a black woman when black lives do not. matter."

Case Figure 3 CMT and the Integration of Mindfulness

CMT Directive

In the next creative activity entitled the CMT and the Integration of Mindfulness, the counseling student was asked to create a follow-up piece of art about the experiences since the previous counseling supervision meeting. Case Figure 6.9 is titled *"Unraveling"* and was created with various colors and gauges of yarn, string, and a wooden dowel. The description that was provided was based on the time that had elapsed from the last meeting to the more recent meeting. The counseling student described the artwork as: "Since our last conversation, I have been sitting with my need to destroy and deconstruct in my creative process. I have also been trying to wrap my mind around how this process plays out and is necessary for my relationships. It has been fascinating. One word that has resonated with me lately is "unraveling," and I find it connects with our conversation. I have been watching a show in which the main character has mentioned a few times that she feels as if she is unraveling or coming undone. I loved the wording of this. I am reminded of a beautiful, though possibly difficult, process when I think of this.

I wanted to merge the two—thoughts of needing to destroy and of unraveling into this piece. I consciously chose to lean into my color coral palette with this one. Making another tapestry piece felt the most obvious choice. When starting this piece, I set out with the intention to keep it smaller. I think I am finding that I can allow my artwork to be busier when I keep it in a small space. I can have more going on, and I enjoy having so many different areas and elements to look at within these confined spaces.

While working with the string, I found myself musing with thoughts like, "Is it undone enough?" I caught myself trying to perfect the messiness and make sure it was undone enough at times. I balanced this with acceptance, allowing it to just be and trusting it would turn out how it was intended to turn out. I enjoyed playing with this idea though, I found

Figure 6.9 CMT and the Integration of Mindfulness.
Permission by artist.

it funny and ironic to be aiming at some unconscious level, for a perfectly deconstructed mess—one that was messy but still beautiful. Undone but make it art."

Reflection after the Creative Work

To support the mindfulness approach through a self-reflective manner, the counseling student met for the supervision process and was asked to verbalize insights about the process and observations about the integration of creativity into supervision. After this meeting, the counseling student wrote up a follow-up statement about the CMT process.

"This experience has been incredibly meaningful for me. Through my mindful art practices, I have noticed several changes in myself; some may occur only in the context of my creative process and others may extend beyond this. First, I recognize an increased sense of self-acceptance and self-assurance. When I started this process three months ago, I quickly realized my desire to do it "right"; I wanted to tackle prompts and make art in the "correct" way. I wanted praise for my work, for the final product as well as for the reflective process. I wanted recognition for my use of color and technique. (And so on.)

Now my creative process looks much different. I find inspiration from images in magazines when feeling stuck. I allow myself to find connections between different images and put pictures together in new ways. I am confident that everything I do is how it is meant to be; I see my "artist self" as an extension of the universe, and as such, every brush stroke is intentional. This confidence in myself and in my process is a stark change from the initial anxiety and the pull to people-please that I felt when approaching a project. In fact, I am now inspired to put together collections of my art and consider ways to share them more publicly.

These developments also come with an increased focus on adaptability; when I make a "mistake" or do something I wouldn't typically like, I now find that I ask myself, "How can I make this work?" or "How does this contribute to the larger picture?" This illustrates my more positive approach to problem-solving since previously, I likely would have harped on the "problem" for a significant amount of time or abandoned the project altogether. In this way, this practice has increased my artistic resilience as well.

A second area that I have noticed an improvement in my ability to tolerate and explore difficult emotions. I have noticed an increased tolerance for "negative" effects since starting this practice. I feel increased confidence in my ability to feel and express my emotions. I also feel more confident that I can connect to others through the specific emotional experiences I express in my art. While I may still avoid tasks that invoke difficult feelings at times, I am now able to recognize this habit more quickly. I have also noticed an increased acceptance of my tendency to use avoidance; I feel much more comfortable noticing when I'm avoiding something and I'm able to note it for later, to explore when I'm ready. This is a new insight for me, and I feel proud of myself for this accomplishment.

Overall, I feel that these mindful art practices have reduced my anxiety and increased my self-confidence, self-acceptance, flexibility, and emotional awareness. I feel I am better equipped to feel and process more emotions now than before I started this mindfulness practice. My creative process also allows me to impress myself frequently in new ways—just yesterday I was impressed by my skill set and ability to illustrate a scene I had in my head. I truly enjoy the process as well as the ability to learn these new things about myself, meet these new parts of myself. I feel like I am a better friend to myself now more than ever.

As you can see, I think this is an incredibly effective process. I think there are significant benefits from using mindful art interventions, and I would love to be able to share all the good things I've gotten from this process with others. I would also love to learn to use this in my own clinical practice, though I still have several questions to explore before I feel prepared to implement this in session. I think the downside for me was the cost of supplies. I tend to be an impulsive buyer and so I spent a lot on new paints, notebooks, brushes, and so on, as I got more into my creative process. As a clinician, I would be concerned about keeping the cost low and what supplies clients may have access to during pandemic times. I am also concerned about the feelings that may come up for clients during this process and clients' abilities to self-regulate during the days between sessions. I have a couple of clients now with a history of self-harm and suicidality who are artistically inclined but who may not be ready for this process if they don't yet have healthy coping skills in practice."

Case Figure 4 CMT and the Traumatized Client Process

CMT Directive

The CMT directive was offered to an 18-year-old adolescent female after having experienced a traumatic response to an assault several months prior. CMT and the Traumatized Client Process and written story. Figure 6.10 pen and ink image are drawn on a small notepad to represent the people around the falling stick figure who are helping the stick figure from falling. The CMT directive was provided and the client quickly completed the piece, and the client wrote the accompanying story to represent the feelings connected to the artwork. The client indicated the piece of writing and accompanying artwork was titled *"Falling"* and was created using the materials of pen and paper and colored pencils. "The experience represented the surrounding support around someone after something like that happens but too foggy-headed to realize the assistance and stability they are offering. It represents a dark period with seemingly no glimmer of light or hope, even though it has been there the whole time and patience with oneself in finding this motivation."

According to the client "at the time, it felt like nothing was up to me, everyone else was making decisions for me and my own good, but I just needed my own time to heal and figure things out for myself, even if I did not know it at the time. Almost a *'waiting'* period, where you are just getting through the days, but everything is grey. Now, it seems that I knew exactly what was going on with everything around me, but I could not do anything about it. I could not reach out for the help that was there or step on the ledge that would have just helped a little bit and not leave me hanging. Looking back, it is interesting to see the details I recall or what stuck out to be the most- those closest to me being right there and supporting the whole time, never letting go, and all of the background people. The ones who would discuss the incident behind my back when

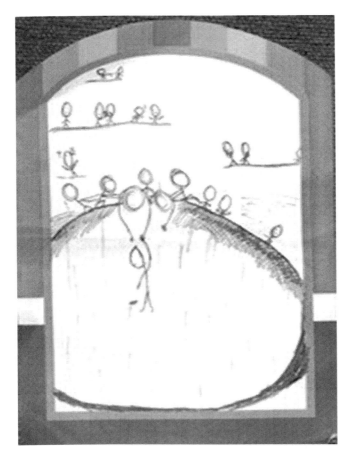

Figure 6.10 CMT and the Traumatized Client Process.
Written Story with Drawn Image.

they did not know any of the truth and rumors just seemed to be spread. Everyone treaded water lightly with me- not knowing where they stand, what to discuss with me, and this sensitive topic, not knowing how to support me if I chose to get emotional in front of them."

"Eventually, I came to realize those background people do not matter at all and those closest to you will support you in your healing and recovery. Even the slightest pull contributed to the whole of the group attempting to keep me from falling in that hole. I learned that I am extremely resilient, and when you come to embrace that it makes you so much stronger. I am strong for even making it this far and can give myself credit for that alone, but to recognize your growth and strength and what you have become from that experience is so extremely fulfilling and empowering."

Reflection after the Creative Work

The client was demonstrating extreme bravery by writing and drawing about the depressive emotions connected to the trauma of assault. The client described it as "sinking into a dark abyss with support attempting to pull back up and ledges to help oneself but no motivation to get out of the hole." The attached image was drawn to reflect the experience and the support received after the trauma event.

Case Figure 5 and Journaling for Self-Reflection

CMT Directive

The CMT and Journaling for Self-Reflection activity represent the thoughts and images experienced throughout the month. The client was utilizing the creative process to assist in the self-reflective process and titled it *"Month Long Bullet Journal Week in Review"* in Figure 6.11. The intentions were to learn to combine journaling and collage, which "provided more freedom to express emotions, allowed for forgiveness for

Figure 6.11 CMT and Journaling for Self-Reflection. Permission provided by Artist.

mistakes and helped to create a sense of structure and reflection to the week. A great exercise when feeling very lost during quarantine/helps ground me/establish a weekly routine. The experience felt very focused when making it. Loose structure, but I make sure to include goals and positive aspects for each week. Include a song of the week as well to add a bit of fun (expressive therapy)."

Reflection after the Creative Work

The client identified how the random writing spaces assist in taking off the pressure from the writing for a school-based approach. The client identified how it felt "more organic and conductive for my thoughts on the week which are usually very scattered and disjointed." The writing reflection provided a space to support some sense of dissociation and safely reflect on the actions and feelings of the week. The client acknowledged that a "finished page is fun to look at and a small-time capsule of the week." By engaging in this process, the themes are personalized to "fit the mood."

Case Figure 6 and Figure 7 CMT and the Trauma Approach with Mindfulness

CMT Directive

The counseling client is a retired female who is single, lives alone, and has a long trauma history and physical pain concerns that impact her health and daily functioning levels. She regularly practices mindfulness to reduce the pain her body experiences, and paints with acrylic paints on various objects including canvas, cardboard, and paper to "keep her body active." The client stated that *Figure 6.12* is entitled *"The Sounds of Silence"* which is an old Simon and Garfunkel song. The client discussed the experience of sitting and "looking at the back yard on a winter night and I painted what I felt."

Another example of a mindful moment is represented in *Figure 6.13* in which the client was asked to identify the areas of importance from a cognitive standpoint and from an emotional standpoint. The words written on a paper towel represented the powerful experiences connected to each of those words including health, work, money, people's behaviors, and meds [medications]. The categories opened the talking points and allowed the client to share in the cognitive and emotional experiences related to mindfulness. The experiences assisted the client in reconnecting and redistributing the powerlessness the client felt. The client was empowered by this redistribution of power and it served to empower resilient methods of thinking and feeling. Through this process, the clients are integrating new corrective experiences with alterations in the neural pathways.

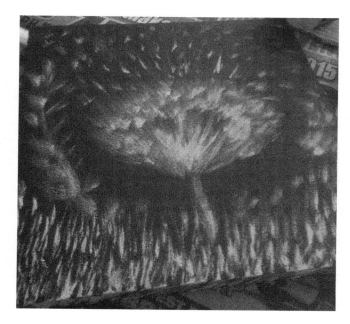

Figure 6.12 CMT and Journaling for Self-Reflection.
Permission provided by Artist.

Reflection after the Creative Work

Both pieces of art represent the client's individual approach to utilizing mindfulness to reduce the emotional stress experienced on a daily basis and to minimize the physical pain and awareness of her cognitive needs. The consistent practice of the mindfulness skills and approaches can become a powerful tool in building resiliency levels and supporting positive interventions for the clients.

Case Figure 8 CMT and Creative Writing for Professional Development

CMT Directive

The counseling student was asked to creatively discuss her professional development as a counselor and to explore professional self-awareness approaches that are common to counselor training. The student chose a creative writing narrative that most connected to her professional development. "To me, it was an expression of the growth and change that has happened in me since beginning this master's degree program." This is a case example of the use of creative writing for professional self-awareness purposes.

Figure 6.13 CMT and the Trauma Approach with Mindfulness. Permission provided by the Artist.

Like a Tree Case Figure 8

The dark, hidden roots of a budding tree take credit for its growing
They are responsible, after all, for what the tree is showing.
They anchor it into the hard, cold ground, they feed it and hydrate it.
The roots don't let it wander far when the wind attempts to take it.
There's an image in my mind of a worn and weathered tree.
It holds onto its roots, but it has lost every single leaf.
The roots are deep and tangled in the soil's massive rocks.
The soil gives life to the weathered tree, but it can't turn back the clock.
The tree has stood for a hundred years. From sapling to mature.
Now this stunted tree cannot provide. It seems much less secure.

A farmer comes to check his crop, the tree is just surviving.
The farmer kneels down, touches the dirt, and licks his finger, smiling.
The soil is good, the tree is big, but it's tired and it's empty.
The tree is standing, but it's not thriving. Something big seems missing.
The farmer leaves with a plan and comes back with some tools.
He asks the tree for its time, and he shares with it the rules.
"It seems to me; this root is wrong. It has crept up to the surface.
It has wrapped around your trunk, keeping you quite burdened.
You're not broken, you are stuck. This root, it has you starving.
I can help you get your food, but it'll take some carving.
Just give us a little time to get you to your best
This might hurt, and you'll have to help, but it'll give you rest."
He starts to poke and prod and pull. The tree can sense the changes.
It's tired and it's scared, and the carving is not painless.
The farmer shows the tree his tools and tells him to hang on,
"I've almost moved this stubborn root, then we can carry on."
The root is strong and holding on to the giant trunk of the tree.
The root cuts into the tree's layers, deeper than the eye can see.
The farmer saws and carves all day, but the root just does not budge.
The tree is tired, worn and weak. That's when it starts to judge.
"You're wasting all of my time and yours. There really is no purpose
In working all your life away, I'm sure I'm just not worth it."
The farmer breathes out a sigh and takes the deepest breath,
He swallows the lump inside his throat, and this is what he says,
"That is not what I believe, it simply isn't true.
Every tree is important, including trees like you.
You give fruit and breath and shade, and you are home to many,
We're almost there, the root is loose, tomorrow will you be ready?"
The tree nods and says "farewell". The farmer packs his tools.
Tomorrow came and went and the work still wasn't through.
Once the trunk was freed from the root, there was a giant ring,
The tree had grown over the root, without it there was a sting.
The bark-less ring around the tree made it quite exposed,
but the farmer did not leave the tree for good until the gap was closed.
It took months and months of work, grafting and deciding
What should stay and what should go, but the tree finally felt like trying.
Then one day the farmer saw that the tree had grown a fruit.
It was big, bright and shiny and round, and it had lots of juice.
"Thank you, farmer, for what you have done! Look, I'm growing fruit."
"Tree! All I did was hold the tools. The real work was in you."

When I squint, and if I'm open, I see that tree is me
The roots are where I came from, and the juicy fruit is what's meant to be.
I'm not who I was, or who was mine. I'm the result of a lot of work.
I grew and things got difficult, and difficult things do hurt.
Unlike the tree, I can run, and run is what I did.
I tried to leave my roots, ignore them, that mistake was big.
My roots can't be un-grown or left, they're somewhere deep inside me.
But I can see parts of them now, I think, and now I'm finished hiding.
The power is in me to heal. To patch up the exposed.
To graft on things that feed my growth, and then move forward and grow.
The ones who checked my soil and then offered to help carve me
Knew my value, knew my worth. They fed me when I was starving.
This journey's been hard. It has made me look at all the things I fear.
My past has holes that I fell in. I've been climbing out all of these years.
I have learned how to look at holes, and rogue roots, and the wind.
Things are going to happen, it's what we do with them.
The trees that grow near me on my professional journey
Will be less judged, more focused on, and become a part of my learning.
I no longer see future clients as people worse off than me.
We're all the same, we all feel pain, the wind blows off our leaves.
But leaves grow back from the inside out. Duct tape won't reapply them.
It's worth the work, the sawing, carving, grafting, and the crying.
Introspection is hard, uncomfortable, and makes us exposed.
But bringing hidden roots to light, can spur a mind to growth.
I'm grateful for this journey, to counselor, to farmer.
I know when I have finished, I'll still go much farther.
Like a tree, we're always growing. We're leafless, then we bloom.
We're never finished growing, and neither are our roots.

Self-Reflection after the Creative Work

The counseling student stated "I see myself as both the tree and the farmer. The farmer's countertransference represents my biggest fear as a counselor- that I might fail my clients in some way. Recognizing this fear and how emotionally drained I could become as a result of carrying the weight of not failing gave me a better understanding of my role as a counselor. The client's problems are not mine to solve. The clients must do the work. I am only there to offer support and guidance. Writing this piece was quite cathartic. I love trees- the way they grow, how they sleep in the winter and even the way that they collect nutrients when they look most lifeless. They are magical, and I think that we have so much in common with them. We grow and thrive in times when we are the body bare and leafless. We collect nutrients in our cold and dark seasons. We grow!"

Case Figure 9 CMT and Poetry for Self-Awareness

A counseling student participated in the process of writing a poem about the reflective processes involved in the developmental process. The directive was to *create an example of your journey through a counseling program.* The counseling student chose to write a poem that connected various ideas that they had been working on for themselves. The poem discussed the key aspects of counselor development and self-awareness for growth including affecting change, newness, vulnerability, and gradually growing into the role of counselor.

An Uncovering Case Figure 9

A mid-life questioning
From macro to micro
From activist to ally
From How do I affect
Change. Be change.
Change.
Embrace the strange and new
Blinking at my own image
Neat rectangles
pulsing beats of humanity
Strangers become friends
Seeing more of me
Uncovering more of me
Arc of a graduate program
Hungry doubt
Knowledge thirsty
Will I be good enough
Identity explored
Competence blooms
Skills on repeat
Practice and pack
the toolbox
Counselor in training
Becomes
Willing Self to be seen

Open up the personal Pandora
Box of insights
Unpack and know thyself
Triggers and trauma
Suffering and addiction
Pain uncovered
Broken attachments
Unconscious desires searing
Vulnerability
Self as conduit
Repository for change
Wanting to help
Change the system
Ended up changing
The scaffolding
Parts, layers, core
Enter the room
Sit with another human being
Here sits my wholeness
My best shot at change
Offering self
Offering hope
Seeing
Listening
Validating
A good enough therapist

Reflections After the Creative Work

After the student created the poem, they were asked to write about the experience. Through expressive writing techniques, the counseling student wrote about the experiences and titled the experiences below.

Here is the written feedback after the writing of the poemAn Uncovering

"Reflecting at the halfway mark. A mid-life decision to affect change, be the change, change. An embrace of the unknown- fears, inadequacies, anxiety. A bearing-down recognition that time is finite, the clock is running down. Back to the classroom at 56. Academia dressed in black and white. Clarity resides in the unrolling of expectations, standards, goals. Fixed points in time to revisit my perfectionism, failures, and desire for legitimacy- a graded snapshot of my worth.

Then, the unexpected. Scrambling to catch up with the world. Technology, language, learning, and unlearning. Hours spent staring at 12 neat rectangles in a matrix holding pulsing beats of humanity, complicated lives behind talking heads. Small momentous decisions. Do I raise my hand? Do I unmute and jump in? How much do I share? The practiced mask of professionalism is chipped away, bit by bit as I learn to cultivate an authenticity that removes the remove, opens a door to being seen. Another generation leads the way, I am finding new ways to access vulnerability. Unpacking the layers and allowing parts of self to be seen and validated. Strangers become friends as we navigate the surprisingly intimate shared space. The intake of knowledge and skills balanced with the slow uncovering of self.

We debate ethics and unveil microaggressions. We express disappointment and rage with institutions and systems slow to change. We wonder at the whiteness of our digital canvas and call ourselves to the task. Confronting racial identity, the unconscious, attachments, and addictions, there are singular moments of shared pain and suffering, the echo of a classmate's voice in my headphones calls forth a Rogerian response. Empathy imprints itself and I catch a glimpse of the meaning-making I want to bring to this work. We absorb the theoretical constructions of self, practice the skills of sitting with another's wounds, packing the metaphorical toolbox with methods and modalities that will help us help others.

A year in, truths emerge. Counselor and Client. 55 minutes of connection. What could possibly make me competent to witness another human's pain? The barrage of information narrows down to elemental insights. The Self as a conduit, the relationship becomes the paradigm for change. Presence. Genuineness. Empathy. Positive regard. A Rogerian ethos at the essence of seeing and connecting. It's the fertile soil from which good therapy becomes possible.

I cling to that trifecta of authentic behavior as I begin my practicum. As theories swirl and modalities compete, I turn towards my own humanity as the truest best thing to offer. In the past year, I have been tasked with self-reflection, an honest accounting of my choices and their roots in the past, my unconscious. I've been asked to do my own work, uncovering and unpacking hard truths. In a sense, I feel newborn. Defenses laid bare, a new empathy for my parts, my survival, my attempts to find my way back to self. With that clarity, I move into a space of unknowing, leaving the intellect and the analyzing, finding a new place where I can meet another with openness, curiosity, respect, and a sense of hope."

Follow up Self-Reflection (One Month Later)

The counseling student followed up one month later with some further thoughts and emotions about the creative writing process. "As I reside here, at an axis between knowledge and intuition, my professional identity begins to take shape. The self emerges and yearns to speak. There is space to be imperfect, to react and defend, to be wholly human. It's there I will do my best work. It's there I will bear witness and offer the hope that lies in change. Awareness and acceptance is a worthy journey. It is my path to becoming a good enough therapist. It's a path that has no end. I've chosen well."

"Bringing mindfulness to the creative process helped me to understand the way my own personal expression of self-manifests through poetry. There are parts of me that negate or minimize my desire to practice creativity and my essence remains hidden behind intellectual engagement or the pursuit of perfectionism. Through this exercise, I was able to allow myself to emerge and achieve a kind of flow on the page. Part of me was not satisfied with the work, but a bigger part of me said, let it be. I felt driven by a truer voice, one rooted in acceptance and insight. It was an opportunity to let myself speak."

CMT Conclusions

Mental health treatment in a trauma-filled world is challenging and leaves many counselors asking for more diverse and effective therapeutic interventions. Clinicians will need to engage in a clinically informed and ethically responsible approach to the emotional and behavioral volatility caused by the trauma exposure, and the subsequent long-term ramifications. Counselors, supervisors, counseling students, and creative individuals alike can effectively incorporate creativity into their professional work. Through a neurobiologically-informed examination of interventions, and consideration of material choice and presentation, we explored effective approaches for clinical work with traumatized clients.

The goal of this book was to operationalize understanding of the processes involved in Creative Mindfulness Techniques. Used in tandem with the workbook, the *Healing from Clinical Trauma Using Creative Mindfulness Techniques* (Costello & Short, 2021) serves as a psychodynamic and evidenced-based counselor resource guide for Creative Mindfulness Techniques (CMT). The impact of the trauma experienced on the body and the brain, and the safety of the individual is considered in the presentation of all creative activities, the impact of the trauma exposure, and the actions of building strength-based approaches to resiliency are examined as well.

As Stephen Porges (2011) discussed "the nervous system continually evaluates risk" (p. 11) which makes it more difficult for traumatized individuals' neuronal pathways to determine safe versus life-threatening situations. However, we have found various methods available to strengthen an individual's sense of self while engaging in the processes of trauma awareness and recovery. Of consideration was taking an intentional and proactive approach to the reduction of the negative impact of future trauma exposures. The impact of harm can be reduced by understanding the neurophysiological activation of the human brain and effectively managing the human drive for survival and nervous systems activation.

By exploring the effectiveness of CMT we are seeking applicable techniques to enhance and support the therapist's toolbox for clinical effectiveness. Client-focused and supervision-focused approaches were provided, and considerations and exclusionary concerns were also addressed. The interventions presented to support the strengthening of resiliency and wellness in the clinical experience of trauma work. Connor and Davidson (2003) identified resiliency as the process of one adapting "body, mind, and spirit to current life circumstances" (p. 76), despite the presence of internal and external factors.

As we better understand the evolutionary processes of the human brain through the anthropological exploration of historic art and expression over time. Evolution was considered from a developmental lens and we have examined the processes inherent in the human species and interventions considered for neurophysiological alteration of the trauma brain. Our discussion turned to the impact of trauma on the individual, on the community, and on the world. With so many opportunities for exposure, mental health professionals need to be cognizant of the impact trauma has on the world and the cultural considerations, on the clients we work with, and on the professionals providing support.

In fact, Siegel (2010) identified that adults with "markedly contrasting culturally shaped experiences, the mature brain in each environment would have responded to the energy and information flow with strikingly different neural connections" (p. 261). Cultural experiences are imprinted in our human neuronal pathways. As our discussion continued, we recognized how the trauma story and the impact of racism and oppression may also be convoluting the trauma story and conflicting the values presented by the traumatized individual. This disconnect may greatly impact the proper diagnosis, treatment setting, and goal setting of individuals from different cultural and migrant populations. This is "in part due to linguistic, religious and social variation from the clinician providing care" (Bhugra & Becker, 2005, p. 18).

The discussion led to the long-term impact of trauma exposure on the physical body and the emotional consequences from adverse childhood experiences or (ACES) which alters the neuronal brain structures. Various researchers have explored alternative approaches to stress reduction and stress inoculation techniques. Many of these approaches incorporated the use of breathing and mindfulness. Dan Siegel (2007) discussed the results of mindful awareness on the various regions of the brain. He stated, "we are stimulating neuronal activity and growth in our own brain by focusing attention on our own intentions" (p. 291). The activation of the axonal fibers at the prefrontal region engages the link to other regions of the brain that includes the cortex, the limbic area, and the brain stem which is impactful in emotional healing. From here, we began altering the perspective of trauma from a negative experience to one of empowerment and strength-based considerations.

Many other researchers have combined approaches for the long-term self-care of their clients. Rappaport (2014) combined "mindfulness practices and the expressive arts [to] teach us how to become aware of the inner witness while noticing and sensing our experience at the same time" (p. 25). Combining approaches of creativity and mindfulness allows for more self-reflection and opportunities for long-term self-care. Meditation has been utilized as a practice for transformative purposes of self-development and creativity according to Horan (2009). Ultimately, the act of creative exploration is a viable method for self-expression, learning, and for personal and professional growth (Claxton, 2006; Coholic, 2011).

By incorporating creative approaches, the individuals are provided "a mental platform for creative breakthroughs and unexpected insights" (Goleman, 2013, p.42). The research discusses how the concept of *flow* can be incorporated into emotional healing. *Flow* is the intensity in the subjective state of people who are completely involved in something in which they forget time, fatigue, and everything else, but the activity. Because the nervous system of humans is constructed to process small amounts of information at a time, *flow* represents the optimal experience that involves a manageable balance between the abilities and opportunities for action by the individual.

Mental health clinicians can effectively utilize a CMT approach through the "process of attunement, or affiliation with another human being which activates mirror neurons between the cingulate and the OFC (orbitofrontal cortex), creates an empathic environment and inhibits the amygdala" (Scaer, 2012, p. 142). The amygdala is holding the emotional memory of the traumatic experience. The therapeutic process is leading to the felt sense which is "the usually unconscious background somatic and visceral sensations that tell us how we are in the moment" (Scaer, 2012, p. 142). Through this process and in conjunction with the physical movement and the emotional energy expelled, therapeutic experience allows for self-reflective learning and self-awareness.

According to Lusebrink (2004), the process of art expression utilizes the "tactile-haptic and visual sensory and perceptual channels" and then is processed through "cognitive and verbal channels" (p. 125). The tactile-haptic refers to the peripheral stimulation created by various sensory experiences or the impact from the spontaneous expression of emotions.

Complex cognitive areas are impacted including the sensory, motor, or verbal areas of the brain.

We have focused on the strength-based approaches that lead to resiliency as we have identified available processes for emotional healing and resistance-building to the trauma impact. Through the incorporation of creative and mindful approaches to strengthen the resilience levels of individuals, we have examined effective approaches to strengthen an individual's sense of self while engaging in the processes of trauma awareness and recovery. The CMT approach aims to increase insight and opportunities to build evidence-based approaches to strengthen the resiliency levels in traumatized individuals. A powerful approach to empower, inform, and support your clinical efforts of treating the traumatized client with alternative and evidence-based interventions.

References for Chapter 6

Bhugra, D., & Becker, M. A. (2005). Migration, cultural bereavement, and cultural identity. *World Psychiatry, 4*(1), 18–24.

Claxton, G. (2006) Cultivating creative mentalities: A framework for education. *Thinking Skills and Creativity, 1*, 57–61.

Coholic, D. A. (2011). Exploring the feasibility and benefits of arts-based mindfulness-based practices with young people in need: Aiming to improve aspects of self-awareness and resilience. *Child Youth Care Forum, 40*, 303–317.

Connor, K. M., & Davidson, J. R. T. (2003). Development of a new resilience scale: The Connor-Davidson resilience scale (CD-RISC). *Depression and Anxiety, 18*, 76–82.

Costello, C. (2015). *Developing resiliency practices in master's level counseling students through creative mindfulness training: An exploratory study.* ProQuest Dissertations Publishing.

Costello, C., & Short, B. A. (2021). *Healing from clinical trauma using creative mindfulness techniques.* New York, NY: Routledge and Press.

Gladding, S. T. (2011). *The creative arts in counseling.* Alexandria, VA: The American Counseling Association.

Goleman, D. (2013). *Focus: The hidden driver of excellence.* New York: Harper Collins.

Horan, R. (2009). The neuropsychological connection between creativity and meditation. *Creativity Research Journal, 21*(2–3), 199–222.

Lusebrink, V. B. (2004). Art therapy and the brain: An attempt to understand the underlying processes of art expression in art therapy. *Art Therapy: Journal of the American Art Therapy Association, 21*(3), 125–135.

Parr, G. D., Montgomery, M., & DeBell, C. (1998). Flow theory as a model for enhancing student resilience. *Professional School Counseling, 1*(5), 26–31.

Porges, S. W. (2011). *The polyvagal theory: neurophysiological foundations of emotions, attachment, communication, and self-regulation* (Norton series on interpersonal neurobiology). New York: WW Norton & Company.

Rappaport, L. (Ed.). (2014). *Mindfulness and the arts therapies: Theory and practice.* London: Jessica Kingsley Publishers.

Scaer, R. (2012). *Eight keys to brain-body balance.* New York: W. W. Norton.

Siegel, D. (2007). *The mindful brain: Reflection and attunement in the cultivation of well-being.* New York: W.W. Norton & Company.

Siegel, D. (2010). *The mindful therapist: A clinician's guide to mindsight and neural integration.* New York: W.W. Norton.

Ulman, E. (2001). Art therapy: Problems of definition. *American Journal of Art Therapy, 40*(1), 16–26

Appendix A
Creative Mindfulness Training for Counselor Development

This CMT research study conducted in 2014 explored the use of mindfulness and creativity for counselor training and wellness. The overarching theme was to explore different methods of increasing counselor awareness and reflective thought while engaging in the process of counselor education. Each week consisted of mindful training with intentional breathing, body relaxation, and awareness of biofeedback considerations such as heart rate and body tension. Each week, the participants were provided an active dialogue training topic that focused on education of counseling concerns (trauma exposure, resiliency, and strength-based considerations). Each week, the artistic expression focused on a specific topic related to self-reflection and counseling.

Week 1
- Mindful Training with intentional breathing, relaxation of the body, and awareness of biofeedback such as heart rate and body tension
- Active Dialogue Training on *Trauma/Vicarious Trauma/ Coping/ Wellness/ Resiliency*

Artistic Expression
- Create an artistic expression about coping, wellness, and resiliency with a title and a written description

Week 2
- Mindful Training with intentional breathing, relaxation of the body, and awareness of biofeedback such as heart rate and body tension
- Active Dialogue Training on *being a counselor and relevant personal strengths*

Artistic Expression
- Create an artistic expression on being a counselor and strengths with a title and a written description

Week 3
*   Mindful Training with intentional breathing, relaxation of the body, and awareness of biofeedback such as heart rate and body tension
*   Active Dialogue *on What did a client stimulate in you that you want to nurture?*

Artistic Expression
*   Create an artistic expression on nurturing with title and written description

Week 4
*   Mindful Training with intentional breathing, relaxation of the body, and awareness of biofeedback such as heart rate and body tension
*   Active Dialogue *on How has your outlook on life changed since becoming a counselor?*

Artistic Expression
*   Create an artistic expression on your outlook on life since becoming a counselor with title and written description

Week 5
*   Mindful Training with intentional breathing, relaxation of the body, and awareness of biofeedback such as heart rate and body tension
*   Active Dialogue *on What does spirituality look like for you?*

Artistic Expression
*   Create an artistic expression about spirituality with title and written description

Week 6
*   Art display of all visual and artistic expressions created for the five previous meetings.
*   Lay out the artwork for display and engage in the interpersonal process with the artist
*   *Identify themes and observations that lead to thematic development and case conceptualizations related to the artist*

Write up
*   Have artist write up those final thoughts about the self-reflective experience

Appendix B
Mindfulness Meditation Script

Get comfortable on the seat or the floor. Plant your feet firmly on the ground and take a big deep breath and relax, with your eyes open or closed. Be aware of sounds coming and going and let them be whatever they are. Know that you are taking this time to meditate. You can drop all other concerns during this period, like setting down a heavy (bag) (box) (load) before plopping into a comfortable (chair) (couch) (bed). After the meditation, you can pick those concerns up again-if you want to.

Bring your awareness to the sensation of breathing. Don't try to control the breath; let it be whatever it is. Sense the cool air coming in and warm air going out; the chest and belly rising and falling.

Try to stay with the sensations of each breath from beginning to end. You may want to softly count your breaths – count to ten and then start over; go back to one if your mind wanders – or note them quietly to yourself as "in" and "out". It's normal for the mind to wander, and when it does, just return to the breath. Be gentle and kind with yourself. See if you can stay attentive to ten breaths in a row. After your mind settles down during the first minutes of the meditation, explore becoming increasingly absorbed in the breath and letting go of everything else. Open to the simple pleasures of breathing, given over to the breath. With some practice, see if you can stay present with the breath for dozens of breaths in a row.

Using the breath as a kind of anchor, be aware of whatever else is moving through the mind. Be aware of thoughts and feelings, wishes and plans, images, and memories – all coming and going. Let them be what they are; don't get caught up in them; don't struggle with or get fascinated by them. Have a sense of acceptance – even kindness – toward whatever passes through the open space of awareness.

Keep settling into the breath, perhaps with a growing sense of peacefulness. Be aware of the changing nature of what passes through the mind. Notice how it feels to get caught up in the passing contents of awareness and how it feels to let them go by. Be aware of peaceful, spacious awareness itself.

In the next few moments, we will bring this meditation to an end. Notice how you feel and take in the good of your meditation. Allow yourself to enjoy those feelings throughout the rest of your day.

Follow up questions for corrective mindfulness techniques:
What is the title for this piece and why?
What was this self-expression process like for you?
Tell me a story about this image?
How did your body respond to this process?
If you were to do this again, what would you change about the experience?

Appendix C

The Formal Steps of CMT: As presented in *Healing from Clinical Trauma Using Creative Mindfulness Techniques*

1. Being in the moment: the client will choose which is best for them at the time

   1. Discussion around what they have brought in with them
   2. Short free write (e.g. the first words that come to mind)
   3. Image or word association using tools provided by therapist

2. Grounding: the client will choose which tool is best for them in the moment (may coincide with step 1 and again after step 3 if needed)

   1. Essential oils or other scented item to ground
   2. Herbal tea
   3. Touch (e.g. have items available which might include textured fabric, wood, stone)
   4. Musical instrument (e.g. singing bowl, chime, drum)
   5. Choose a color swatch to hold and look at

3. Mindfulness interventions: the client will choose which is best for them at the time

   1. Meditation activity
   2. Guided imagery
   3. Breath work (may be used in conjunction with meditation or guided imagery)

4. Response art: the clinician will suggest art materials and directive based on knowledge of client's needs, struggles, strengths, and presentation after a brief check in after the mindfulness intervention. The client will create in structured time that therapist gently monitors

5.   Reflection and process

1.   The client/artist will sit with the piece and consider the experience.
2.   The client and the therapist will explore what came up in the experience.

Index